You Say Tomato

You Say Tomato

The Transatlantic correspondence of
George and Brad

by Adrian Plass and Paul McCusker

Marshall Pickering
An Imprint of HarperCollins*Publishers*

Marshall Pickering is an Imprint of
HarperCollins*Religious*
Part of HarperCollins*Publishers*
77–85 Fulham Palace Road, London W6 8JB

First published in Great Britain
in 1995 by Marshall Pickering

10   9   8   7   6   5   4   3   2   1

A catalogue record for this book is
available from the British Library

ISBN 0 551 02983 8

Typeset by Harper Phototypesetters Limited
Northampton, England
Printed and bound in Great Britain by
HarperCollinsManufacturing Glasgow

To Bridget, for the cups of tea and coffee, the taxi service, the nights around the kitchen table, and her endless warmth and love.

And to Elizabeth, for her long-distance patience and love from five thousand miles away.

Introduction

Have you ever looked at yourself and Christians around you and thought: what a strange group of people we are? Have you ever felt angry or confused, but tried to hide your feelings because being honest about them wouldn't seem Christian? Have you ever wondered if other Christians – even Christians in another country – felt the same way you do? If so, then this collection of letters may be a comfort to you.

George Smith, an Englishman, and Brad Miller, an American, first met at a conference in England. For reasons unknown (considering their very different personalities), their relationship endured beyond the conference itself to an evening of extensive chatting at a local pub. Brad climbed aboard a plane for America the next day and the distance gave birth to these letters.

As you'll see in the pages that follow, George and Brad believed that extracts from their transatlantic correspondence might become a series of humorous articles (hopefully a book) about Christianity in England and the United States. Imagine trying to explain the Church of England to an American. Or the David and Goliath Day Care and Whole Armor of God Christian School to an Englishman. George and Brad made the attempt and, as a wry look at the cultural differences of their respective countries, they succeeded. The resulting articles were quite popular with readers of *Today's Christian World* magazine.

But the story didn't end there. As we the editors, sorted through the unabridged letters for this book, we discovered that there was more going on than just clever observations about England and America. George and Brad's personal differences seemed to literally play out the differences between their two countries. Words and phrases didn't translate, simple ideas were misunderstood, and the chasm of manners and norms wreaked havoc on the purest intentions. It was as if they lived out a comedy of errors while trying to write about a comedy of errors.

But the letters go deeper still. Readers get a personal look into the lives of these two men during what proved to be an especially difficult time for both of them. There's a lot of pain, change and honesty next to the humour. For example, readers who are familiar with C. S. Lewis's state of mind at the beginning of A *Grief Observed* will recognize the anger and confusion George expresses in his early letters. His honesty is downright intimidating and demands that the reader pay attention – just as Brad had to do. Similarly, Brad starts off on a sure-footing of what he believes about Christianity, but soon learns that there's a lot more to himself – and those around him – than he thinks.

Along the way, they deal with the harder questions of life. Where is God when you need him? What does it mean to be a Christian? Exactly what is the Punklethwaite Pant? What does Diane's sweater/jumper have to do with Brad's spiritual growth? And how many pints of bitter can George drink in binary?

Somehow in their mix-ups and miscommunication George and Brad grasp that the boundaries of stars and stripes, fish and chips, colour and color prove superficial at best. There is a common love and faith at the very heart of who they are. In other words, those of us who struggle to genuinely know and love Jesus are united regardless of where we call home.

We believe honest Christians everywhere will identify with these two men and the things they've written.

Adrian Plass and Paul McCusker

[**Editors' Note:** The first piece of correspondence was an undated postcard from Brad to George. The front of the card was a mocked-up photo of the Queen eating a Big Mac at a McDonald's in Windsor. Brad obviously thought this card was very funny since he sent one to each of his friends in America.]

Dear George

Great card, huh?

Thanks for a great time! I'll always remember my last night in England!

Tag. You're it.

Brad

21 April

Dear Brad

Do *you* remember your last evening in England? We settled down for a couple of hours in that cosy little bar on the Gatwick side of Haywards Heath[1] for a final chat before you flew back across the Atlantic.[2] You were particularly generous to your stomach in the course of that evening, I seem to remember (1 Timothy 5:23), while I remained clear-headed and miserable.

I have a misty recollection that, in the context of our rather maudlin conversation, it seemed a good idea to make ridiculous promises to each other about the future. One of them concerned eternal brotherhood, and should obviously be ignored completely (we – or rather, you – having reached the emotional molasses stage by then), but the other was a bit more alarming. When we were at the 'wringing each other's hands and telling each other that we were the most wonderful people in the world' stage, was something said about writing letters? Please tell me I'm wrong, because I feel about as communicative as a dead earthworm. Did I really ask you to explain in detail how the Church works in the United States of Thingummybob? And did I, God help me, promise to become extremely boring on the subject of the Church in England? Am I right? If I am right, then this is my first epistle, and probably my last. You've almost certainly come under the spell of some blow-wave evangelist by now, and can't be bothered with tedious old reality any more. Besides which, these great letter-writing plans almost never actually happen. Anyway, I've written, so I get the blessing and you have to either reply or come under the hammer of God (if he exists).

If by some remote chance you do write back, I shall try to fill you in on the role of the Church in this country (roughly equivalent to that of an elderly relative living in an annex[3] who everybody's forgotten about, but she's going to die soon anyway, so it doesn't really matter). In the meantime, let me tell you a short but instructive story.

When I was a *small* miserable person – about three years old – I was sent to stay with my Great Aunt Elizabeth while something mystifying gynaecological was happening at home. When I arrived at Great Aunt Elizabeth's gothic little semi-detached in north Bromley, I was immediately steered towards the bathroom by my aunt, who I remember as being about fourteen feet tall. Before I went in she gripped my shoulder and bent low to speak to me. Words came out of her vast face and splattered over my small one. 'Do you', she enquired, in marine-avoidance tones, 'want number one, or number two?'

I considered. As I had not the slightest idea what those terms meant, it was not a very easy question to answer. 'Number one, please,' I said, hoping it was a cake.

It was not a cake. Great Aunt Elizabeth pushed me firmly into the bathroom and closed the door behind me. I stood inside for some time, waiting for number one to arrive, but it didn't. So I gave up, went to the lavatory to pass the time, then returned dismally to the sepulchral care of my immense hostess.

I tell you this story, Brad (why do so many Americans have names that sound like something out of a toolbox?), because the description of that experience in the early years of my life is a symbolic, but highly accurate picture of my early experiences of religion in England. Doing things one does not understand in response to terminology that is totally inexplicable, with rather disappointing results, has long been a feature of church life in this country.

If you're not too busy fawning over some gruesome example of the pearly-toothed prison fodder that seems to infest your airwaves, perhaps you could tell me about the Church in your little country.

Yours with mininal hope of a response,

George

P.S. Seriously, Brad, if you do want us to exchange letters, that's fine as long as there's some real point, which I rather doubt.

P.P.S. Cherry sends her love and would have sent the ham sandwich she didn't want to eat if I'd let her.

Notes

[1] The Red Lion, which George and Brad stopped at on the way to Gatwick Airport, where Brad was due to catch a flight back to America the next day. According to Brad's personal diary, he nearly overslept and missed the flight. He had a bad headache (which he insisted was *not* alcohol-related).

[2] Brad went to England as both a freelance writer and to represent several small publishing firms at the International Christian Exhibition (17-20 March) in Eastbourne. George was there to represent his own interests as a freelance writer and publisher of *Hewn Coils*, a monthly periodical of poems.

[3] For American readers, an 'annex' is an addition built on to a house.

April 28th

Dear George

What a surprise! I didn't expect your letter, especially since I
wasn't sure if you'd remember your promise to write. Though
how you stayed 'clear-headed' the night before I left is beyond
me. By any standard of measurement – American or British –
seven pints of bitter [1] is a lot. No wonder your recollection was
'misty'. At the rate you were going, I'm not sure how you
functioned at the ICE [2] at all. I confess, though, that I really
enjoyed those little drinks I had. You know, the ones with the
cucumbers and little umbrellas. What were they called?
Pam's? Pim's? And, please help me, but I have this vague
memory of drinking two and then proposing to the waitress.
Did she say yes? I'll assume those drinks *were* alcoholic (a big
no-no for many Christians in this country. I don't know how
Christians over there get away with it – but I won't tell if you
won't, particularly since it was my first time there.)

You're such a funny guy – the way you put on being so
miserable and acting like you don't *really* want to write. I
guess that's what you call the 'British style of humor', huh?
Bleak, droll, with an obsession about toilets. I've watched
Benny Hill and *Monty Python* enough to know about these
things. But don't act like you don't want to write. You're a
writer, for crying out loud. Well, a *reporter*, [3] at least.

Anyway, a big tally-ho and pip-pip to you George. (You
know, one day you're going to have to explain those
expressions to me. I'm sure there are reasons for their
existence, but I'm bewildered by what those reasons might
be. Scripture references would be helpful.)

I've been thinking about our discussion of the differences between the *American* version of Christianity and the *British* version. It's not an easy task, I hope you know. I mean, until we talked about it, it hadn't occurred to me that our Christianity is any different from yours. I suppose it would have to be, considering all the 'thees' and 'thous' you guys use when you talk. But *explaining* the differences could be a problem. That means I would have to actually *think* through a lot of things I've been taking for granted most of my life.

Thanks, pal.

Okay, when we were together you said that we 'have as many churches in America as Britain has fish-n-chips shops'. I thought that was harsh and unfair, so I decided to do a little checking to prove you wrong. I picked up the Yellow Pages (do you have those? they're phone directories with . . . uh, yellow pages) and flipped to the 'Churches' category. There were ads and phone numbers for 127 churches. I found churches of all stripes: Catholic, Protestant, Charismatic, Liturgical, Orthodox, Unorthodox, and one professing to be totally Unprincipled.

I guess it's been a long time since I looked at church names (mine is a basic Grace Church). I expected the traditional First Baptist Church or St Paul's Methodist Church or Sacred Heart Catholic Church, and there were a few of those. What surprised me was the diversity of the other, less traditional, churches. They had names like the Family Church of the Community, the City Community Church, St Affiliated Church, the Church of the Immaculate Reception, Town & Country Universal Church, the First Church of Infinite Uniformity, and the Home Cell of Unified Saint(s).

How many fish-n-chip shops do you have? I'd like to compare the numbers.

That we have a lot of churches is one thing; *why* we have them was the question I assume you want answered. Like I often do with my Bible study, I closed my eyes and pointed to a line on the page in the directory. It landed on Home Cell of

Unified Saint(s). I went to talk with the pastor there to see if he could explain the whys and wherefores of our abundance of churches. His name was Pat McSwindon.

Instead of a traditional-looking church – or even a church at all – the Home Cell of Unified Saint(s) was a small house in a suburban cluster of small houses just south of town. I don't know whether this seems strange to you or not. Sometimes American Christians worship in homes. Do British Christians ever worship at home? Pat McSwindon answered the door and greeted me with a large smile and a handshake. Now, I want to say first and foremost that I resented you calling our evangelists 'blow-wave', but in this case . . . Well, he was tall and tan, with manicured silver hair that glittered like a precious metal.

I explained to him that I was on a mission for a British friend to discover why America has so many churches. He smiled knowingly, then suggested that his personal testimony might be helpful. He told me that he was once a previously-owned vehicle marketing specialist (used-car salesman) in nearby Brownfield until circumstances forced him to start the Home Cell of Unified Saint(s). I took notes for your benefit:

'It started because I used to be an elder at my other church,' he explained. 'But I resigned.'

'Why did you resign?' I asked.

'The double life was too much for me.'

I was intrigued. 'Double life? What – being an elder and a used-car salesman?'

'No. Being an elder and a Christian,' he replied. 'See, being an elder in my church was pretty dirty business. We were heavily involved in what some would call "religious aerobics."'

'Religious aerobics?'

'Church splits,' he smiled. 'In the beginning, we started off as the Citywide Church of Faith, Hope & Love. But half of us got upset over a doctrinal difference.'

'What was the doctrinal difference?' I asked.

'The music director insisted on lime polyester choir robes and we wanted orange,' the Reverend answered. 'So we left to start our own church called the Faith Community Church of Hope & Love. But then the issue of "communion" came up.'

'Communion? Whether to have it or not?'

He shook his head, 'No – whether to use unsalted crackers or unleavened bread. On principle, half of us marched off to become the Neighborhood Church of Hope & Love.'

'You lost "Faith",' I observed.

'Had to,' McSwindon explained. 'Community Church took out a court injunction so we couldn't have "Faith". By this time, we didn't need it anyway.'

I pressed on, 'Then what?'

'A group of us became angry when the pastor began doing announcements at the beginning of the service instead of the traditional place before the offering was taken. So we left to become the True Believers' Assembly of Hope & Love.'

'True Believers?'

He nodded earnestly, 'Yes. When you get to be that small, you figure it's because the Lord is weeding out the chaff, if you know what I mean.'

I said I did even though I didn't. I made a note to look it up in my concordance when I got home.

'Then we lost a section of our congregation because they backslid and returned to Citywide Church,' the Reverend continued. 'To avoid confusion, we put up a big sign saying "Under New Management" and became the House of Love. By this time we lost "Hope".'

'House of Love'?

'That didn't last,' he said. I asked why not. 'We had to change it because we were getting all the right people – for the wrong reasons. Sailors and out-of-town executives, that sort,' he grimaced.

'But what became of your church?'

He gestured to the room around us. 'Now it's just me. I'm

the Home Cell Of Unified Saint(s). I meet in my living room.'

'Amazing.'

'I had a business meeting the other night and elected myself pastor. Got a raise, too,' he said.

At this point, I accidentally broke the lead on my pencil and decided to forgo any further discussion. Does that answer your question?

Now, I have a few of my own. Are you Anglican or Church of England? What does that have to do with your story about using your Great Aunt's bathroom? Or is that more of your 'British style of humor'? And who in the world is Cherry? The name sounds familiar. She isn't the waitress I proposed to, is she?

Tag. You're it.

Brad

Notes:

[1]Bitter here refers to draught beer with a high hop content and a slightly bitter taste.

[2]ICE stands for the International Christian Exhibition, held in Eastbourne, where George and Brad first met.

[3]Brad is mistaken. George is a writer, editor and poet, not a reporter.

11 May

Dear Brad

I thought you Americans prided yourselves on not being suckered. I figured (that's USA for 'thought', isn't it?) that if I made you feel enough of a potential failure you'd be bound to do something about it – and you did. You wrote! I've given up feelings for Lent, but thank you anyway.

Now, having said that, I just need to put you right on one or two things. First of all, I only drink because scripture tells me to. No, not that tired old bit about 'drinking wine for your stomach's sake', but a completely different reference that teetotallers conveniently ignore, especially those who are wretchedly addicted to their abstention. The verse in question appears in Jeremiah 25:27, and it really couldn't be clearer:

> Then tell them, 'This is what the Lord Almighty, the God of Israel, says: Drink, get drunk and vomit, and fall to rise no more . . .'

And then a little further on in verse 28:

> But if they refuse to take the cup from your hand and drink, tell them, 'This is what the Lord Almighty says: You must drink it!'

I have to tell you, Brad (do you prefer Brad or the complete 'Bradawl',[1] by the way?), that every Friday night in this so-called godless country thousands of people are setting out to obey that scripture with as much selfless enthusiasm as they

10

can muster. Yes, I know – you're sitting there in your log cabin across the sea choking on your milk and cookies and spluttering something about 'out of context'. Well, why not? That's how most of those denominations you mentioned got started, isn't it? Well, isn't it?

Anyway, it wasn't seven pints. I counted the number of drinks I had several times, including twice in binary, and I don't think it ever came to seven. Incidentally, *your* drinks were extremely alcoholic, and it wasn't the waitress you proposed to – it was me. I declined. It would take a good many more pints than 111 (seven in binary) before I started to think you were a pretty little thing – but thank you anyway.

You asked me how Christians in this country get away with drinking alcohol. Well, we've all got a bit lost in that area. The great push away from legalism and bigotry has produced quite a little wine-drinking culture among evangelicals. We meet and tell each other how wonderful it is that we're not bound by the chains that imprison all those silly old people who think the road to hell is paved with corks. Of course, we add, if the famous 'weaker brother' should appear in our midst we would immediately and joyfully turn to the raspberryade. How fortunate for the old W.B. [2] that he should fall among brothers in whom strength, charity and adaptability are so abundantly evident. I do drink too much, for reasons that God knows about, even if he doesn't approve of the way I cope.

Speaking of approval – I dare you to read out what I've written here in whichever giant greenhouse you worship at. Go on – I dare you! I bet this letter alone would be enough justification for them to strip you of your third assistant banner-maker position – in love. We have a little problem with public and private morality in the Church over here, and I can't believe it's any different in America. I don't trust anyone except Billy Graham and Cliff Richard. I bet you don't dare read it out.

11   I have to confess, Bradawl, that the account of your

meeting with the odious Pat McSwindon made me laugh very much. But, hell, Brad (think I'd fit in over there?), I'm not in hospital, you know. I'm a writer too. I know fiction when I see it. I don't expect your letters to be a substitute for *Blackadder*[3]. What I'm trying to say is that I want to hear about things that are *really* happening in the Church, and even, Mr Buttoned-up-good-and-proper, things that really happen to you. Come on, feller (is that right?), we nearly got engaged once. I know I'm a bit closed up, but I'm a Mick Jagger yawn compared with you.

Here's a small coin of vulnerability for you to spend any way you like. Cherry is my daughter. She's six and is unique in that she think's I'm wonderful. I told you a lot about her and you forgot every word. I felt hurt and angry when I realized that. Stupid, eh? If she'd been called Pam's or Pimm's you might have remembered her . . .

I'm not answering any more of your questions until you tell me whether you intend to entertain me or write to me. Yes or no?

Yours, not at present in his grip,

George

Notes

[1] A bradawl is a tool for making a hole in wood or leather.

[2] Weaker Brethren.

[3] *Blackadder* was a popular British comedy series known for its biting sarcasm and unmerciful satire. In America, it was frequently seen on certain cable networks and Public Television channels.

May 19th

Dear George

Bradawl?

Obviously I misunderstood what this exchange of letters was supposed to be. The idea that they might be *good natured* was one notion. And I thought they might be *constructive*, too. But the sour-puss attitude you insist on taking makes me wonder otherwise. I had no idea you Brits were so moody.

Okay, I confess that the conversation with Pat McSwindon was fictional, but it was no less true. It's a reasonable representation. In America churches *do* split up over the most petty things. Maybe that's been true of Christians throughout history. I don't know. Y'see, before I got involved in the Church, I was led to believe that we were all just . . . well, *Christians* who just happened to be divided up into various denominations because of theological differences. That's why we have Baptists (who believe in baptism) and Lutherans (who believe in Luther) and Presbyterians (who believe in presbyters) and Pentecostals (who believe in Pentecost) and Assembly of God (who believe in assemblies) and Unitarians (who believe in everything).

I've since discovered that, at least in America, even the denominations are merely sub-divisions of larger divisions. For example, a person can be Baptist or Lutheran and also be an Evangelical. Now, as best as I can figure it, Evangelicals are mainstream-type Christians who believe that Jesus is God, the Bible doesn't have errors and that Christians ought to be against abortion and homosexuality, etc. (You mentioned Evangelicals in your letter and I'd like to know how *you* define them in your country.)

There is another group called Charismatics who believe many of the same things as other Evangelicals – and can be Evangelicals themselves – except they speak in tongues, raise people from the dead and things like that. Now, you also need to understand that Pentecostals are also Charismatics except they like to mess around with snakes [1] and roll in the church aisles during services. (I haven't seen this for myself, but have it from a reliable source.)

Now, you can also have combinations of Christians who are Evangelicals *and* Charismatics but may be liberal or conservative in their general disposition. *Liberal* means that they take a rather liberal view of interpreting the Bible. They think the Bible got a lot of the facts wrong while the spiritual truths are worth listening to. Oh yeah, they're also real big about feeding the poor, letting homosexuals become pastors, revolution in South America, women's rights – and they're the Christians who drink. They're also the only Christians who would watch programs like *Blackadder*, because it's broadcast on the equally liberal Public Broadcasting System. *Conservative*, on the other hand, means they take a rather . . . er, conservative view of the same. I'm not sure what this means except conservatives *want* to feed the poor, but often won't because the liberals are in charge of the programs. To put it in the words of one pastor I know: 'Liberals are probably barely saved (if they're saved at all) while Conservatives are confidently saved (whether they are or they aren't).'

Is this making any sense? Perhaps I should provide line drawings or a graph. What it boils down to is this: you can be an Evangelical *and* a Charismatic *and* Conservative *or* Liberal (but you can't be both at the same time) and *also be* a Baptist or a Lutheran or a Presbyterian. (None of this even comes close to explaining the differences between Catholics and Protestants, but I guess you know all about that since those problems started in your country.)

I'm not sure what I am. Becoming a writer messed everything up for me. On one hand, I feel like I'm too liberal to be a conservative and, on the other hand, too conservative to be a liberal. So, to comment on your rather snide challenge to read to my church that I *accidentally* had too much to drink while in England: well, it wouldn't surprise them. Mostly because I *am* a writer and that's the kind of behavior they expect (Christian or otherwise). We don't hang banners in our church anyway, so there. Drinking's only a big no-no if done to excess. Obviously, by your imbibing, the rules are different. What could a man of your success possibly have to cope with?

As for Cherry . . . Well, I'm sorry. I didn't mean to hurt you or make you feel angry. I remember you talking about her, but I thought you called her *Sherry* and figured it was a dog you had appropriately named after a favorite beverage of yours. You can be sure that I won't forget again after that scolding. I don't remember you mentioning her mother – your wife? Are you divorced or what?

One last question: who is Cliff Richard?

Tag. You're it.

Brad

Notes

[1] Snake-handling (based on a literal application of Mark 16:18) is a practice associated with certain Pentecostal churches in parts of America.

24 May

Dear Bradman

First of all, let me say how thrilled I am that you are (I
assume) named after one of my great cricketing heroes.[1]
Cricket is a game in which nobody moves and nothing
happens but everybody gets very excited, rather like your
Episcopalian church I would imagine – if you leave out the
excitement, that is.

Secondly, I found your pathetic joke about Cherry
extremely offensive, though not quite as offensive, I must
admit, as your crass enquiry about my wife. 'Are you divorced
or what?' you asked. I would hardly dare confess to an
American, least of all one as sensitive as yourself, Bradman,
that I am in that evil and scripturally unsound position. I'm
told you come right off everyone's Christmas card list if
you're careless enough to lose a wife in the land of
opportunity. As it happens I'm not divorced, but my limited
experience of your counselling style (British Rail Train
Enquires could use you) does not encourage me to tell you
what I actually am. Mind your own business.

Thirdly, you ask who Cliff Richard is. He's a singer and the
only famous Christian in the universe, as far as a lot of
people in this country are concerned. Not knowing who Cliff
Richard is, if you're part of the evangelical church in Britain,
is roughly equivalent to announcing that you're getting
divorced in one of those dismal little gatherings of yours
where the members have had compassion removed as if it
was a dysfunctional spleen. Is that the kind of group you go
to, by the way? Speaking of which, your comment about

accidentally drinking too much is such a squeakily defensive ploy. Go back to your pre-fallen-Swaggart clones, or whatever your church group is composed of, and read out the following paragraph:

> Whilst in a bar in England, Brad Miller, who you all know as a good role-playing evangelical who never ever spoilt things by telling the truth before, stood up after finishing his second highly intoxicating drink and said, 'Bearing in mind that there's probably no God after all – at least, not in England, I'm going to get as smashed as I possibly can. I can always go back to being a sober believer when I get home.' He then fulfilled this prophecy to the point of near-horizontality.

Read that out, Bradley Washington.

As to the rest of what you said – well, thanks for the essay. You've obviously given up entertaining me and decided I need a little education. I shall respond to one or two of your comments, and after that I seriously suggest that this correspondence should cease. I'm too vulnerable and you're too closed up for us to ever get anywhere. We're both diseased with flippancy as well, which is bad news for any chance of real forward movement.

You ask me how we define evangelicals – we don't, we castrate them. Over the last twenty years or so the evangelical church, of which I am a jaded and Eeyore-like member, has tried to encase all of human experience into about four phrases. We're just beginning to wake up to the fact that bits of humanity are squeezing out through the cracks and demanding something that fits a bit better. No one's more orthodox than I am underneath all this groaning and spitting, but I want there to be art and life and breadth and ordinariness and weather and light and darkness and *me* in my faith – if I've still got one tucked away somewhere.

As for all the other labels you mention, well, we do have

our own Pentecostals, Charismatics, liberals, etc. all of which are only as good as their genuine involvement with Jesus. Do you love Jesus, Bradman? I think I do somewhere deep inside, despite being so dried up and caustic. Do you love anyone, Bradman?

Homosexuality? Being gay can be almost compulsory or a hanging offence, depending on which group you align yourself with. My own lusts are very straight and ungratified. I suppose, like most Americans, you're in touch with yourself, are you? That's cool.

I don't want to talk about any of this any more, Bradman. Don't write again. It stirs me up, and I don't like it. Maybe see you in England again one day – I prefer you when you're drunk.

George

Notes
¹Donald Bradman was an Australian cricketer, considered by many to be the world's best batsman.

[**Editors' Note:** At this point, several weeks went by without communication. Brad noted in his personal diary on 29 May that he felt confused and angry about George's letter. He couldn't imagine what offence he had committed or why George would treat him so poorly. On 28 June his diary notes only that he decided to write to George again because he hated to leave their relationship on such a sour note.]

June 29t.

Can we get a few things cleared up? First, my name *isn't* Bradawl or Bradman. It's B**rad**, short for B**radley** – which was my mother's maiden name. I hope there's nothing wrong or offensive in that. I mean, good grief, I just can't seem to say anything right with you. I wasn't trying to make a joke about Cherry. I was sincerely confused about who she was. And I can't imagine why it's so crass to ask about your wife. It was an understandable question in light of the fact that you have a daughter. I assumed a wife was involved at some point and simply wondered where she was. What in the world are you so angry about? High alimony payments? What?

For the sake of the friendship I *thought* we had started while I was in England – a certain *bonding*, if you'll pardon the cliché – I won't honor your request that we stop writing. Obviously something needs to be worked out here. If I offended you, then I'm sorry. It was completely unintentional.

Besides, I'm in a jam and I desperately need your help. You see, I mentioned to my editor at *Today's Christian World* (formerly *Today's Christian Family Magazine*, after it was *Christian Family Digest*, but you may have known it as *The Monthly*

Christian Digest & Review) about our correspondence and he thinks it's a great idea. Two Christians from two separate countries explaining their Christianity to each other. He thinks it's worthy of a series of articles – maybe even a book. I can't help but think that it's too good an opportunity for both of us to pass up. And you're the only writer I know in England. Can we call a truce? Can you back off of whatever has you so riled enough to give me some professional reporting about the state of Christianity in Great Britain.?

If you're willing, a good starting place would be your definition of Evangelicals. How do you really categorize Pentecostals, Charismatics, Liberals – and if they are called those names there?

If you're not willing, then I don't know what to say. Except, maybe, it was nice knowing you and I wish you'd help me understand what's gone wrong here. I never claimed to be the most sensitive man in the world, but I never thought of myself as heartless. Are we just miscommunicating?

As for one of your last questions: yes, George, I love Jesus. I don't always know what that means, but I do love him.

I'll wait to hear from you.

Most sincerely,

Brad

7 July

Dear Bradley

I'm very surprised that you've written to me again. I really
thought my last offering would have seen you off good and
proper. Now look what you've done! You've been and gone
and revealed that you're a human being, or at least a Tin Man
who got lucky. I'm sorry I was so hard and harsh, but I haven't
let anyone except Cherry into the middle of myself for a very
long time. The whole business of the Church is so much a
part of the problem that I just couldn't stand the idea of
entering into competition about who could take the mickey [1]
out of religious institutions most effectively and
humourously. I still don't want to do that. But maybe –
maybe something else.

Another thing is that, although I allow myself the freedom
to joke about pretty well anything, I don't like others doing it
when it comes to areas where I'm tender, and the area of my
wife is just about the tenderest one of all. (I notice that, even
in this letter, you couldn't resist the crack about the alimony
payments. Get yourself a Delete button, Bradley.) My wife is
dead – I believe that's scripturally allowable – so Cherry
hasn't had a mum for five years of her life, and I haven't
wanted anyone else. Maybe I'll tell you some more about
that another time, but not yet.

The friendship that *you* thought (did you have a bumper
crop of italics this year or something?) we started in England
was a reality, but my fear of getting close and your apparent
inability to put any heart into your letters gave me cold feet –
until now. But we're both still on probation, Bradley, my man.

Oh, and no, of course I won't pardon the use of a word like 'bonding'. It makes me think of lumberjacks sobbing all over each other. Horrible! So there we are, Bradley. I tentatively accept your apology, and I hope you totally and unconditionally accept mine. By the way, I have to admit that I do enjoy the flippancy, as long as it isn't all we do all the time. Not easy, because it's infectious, a textually communicated disease in fact.

Now we come to your 'jam', and, Bradley, if I find this is the real reason for your sudden burst of humanity I shall come over there, tie you to your bed and make you listen to the whole of A Brief History of Time, which you have undoubtedly bought but never read.[2] Brief will not be the word. Articles or a book, eh? I can't tell you how flattered I am that you should have me at the head of your carefully compiled list of possible collaborators, even if I'm the only writer you know in England. I don't mind having a go if someone thinks it's a good idea, but there are one or two things to bear in mind.

First of all, I'm not an expert in these matters, just a participant. If you want me to talk about what I've heard of what's happened to me in various bits of the Church over here, that's fine, but if you want some kind of informed, organized overview, then you'd better ask God, or David Pawson [3] if you want to go to the very top.

The second thing is that I don't want to end up posing in an epistolary way every time I send you a letter – writing for posterity, as it were. I reserve the right to throw in any old personal rubbish that I like. We can always edit it later. In fact, looking back at our first few letters, I can't imagine any Christian publisher that I know letting some of that material through the abominable filter of what is thought to be 'all right'.

I will tell you what I think about P's and C's and L's, but first of all I demand a hostage. Tell me how you became a Christian, and after that, as Sherlock Holmes would say (tell everyone in America he never really existed, will you?) the 'game's afoot'.

Yours wishing he'd not answered your letter,

George

P.S. Naturally, money is of absolutely no interest to me, but if there's an advance involved with this book I want half.

P.P.S. What is happening to Christian publishing in America anyway? Where will our great work fit?

Notes
[1] 'Take the mickey' is a British expression which means to 'make fun of'.

[2] A *Brief History of Time* is a book by Stephen Hawking which people *did* buy, but no one read.

[3] David Pawson is a leading British Bible teacher.

July 12th

Dear George

Okay, once again Brad has opened mouth and inserted his foot. I'm sorry to hear about your wife. For one stupid reason or another, it hadn't occurred to me that she may have . . . you know. I seem to be surrounded by so many Christian couples who are divorcing lately that I assumed . . . well, never mind. Obviously it was wrong to assume anything. I'm sorry. If I don't have a Delete button on my computer, I'll just run out and buy one now.

About this transatlantic project. I don't think anyone's expecting us to be experts about Christianity in our countries – just representative observers. And right now it's for a series of articles in the magazine I contribute to, not a book publisher. To be honest, I'm not sure any Christian publisher here will go near any of our letters – including the first few. Such is the nature of American Christian publishing. You asked where our book would fit in. Well, unless we turn this into some sort of 'how to' or novel or romance, I don't know who will take the chance. Maybe it's the same there. American Christians enjoy titles like *Ten Steps to a More Effective Prayer-Life* and *Giving Up Spiritual Mediocrity in Five Easy Lessons* and *Finding the Peak of Power while Capturing the Core of Christianity (A Seven-Point Plan)* and *How to be Christlike in the Comfort of your own Home*.

For entertainment, we're inclined towards novels that explore the depths of spiritual warfare like *This Darkest Present* or *Piercing the Prophet* or whatever those books were called. Christian romances are also very popular now, though I don't read them. They generally have to do with a godly woman in peril and the ungodly man who gets saved as a result of some terrible misfortune suffered by the woman on his behalf, or something like that. There always seems to be a large cabin or a boat nearby – that's all I know. Fantasies are also a hot item, come to think of it, mostly because the authors can talk about all kinds of spiritual things without ever being practical about them. A character who is able to vanquish the forces of evil through a Ring of Goodness or a Sword of Truth need never deal with the temptation to call his neighbor a stupid idiot because his oaf of a dog knocked over his trash-can again. Christian fantasies also have a better chance of catching on in the secular market, too.

What was the question?

Oh, whether or not I'll be able to find a publisher for our letters. I honestly don't know. Fact is: if C.S. Lewis wrote the Narnia Chronicles now, no Christian publisher would go near them – what with sensibilities and expectations being what they are these days. I think it's safe to say that the Bible itself wouldn't get beyond the early reviewing stages. What publisher would want to go near a book with over forty unknown authors who were all Middle-Eastern, nomads, fishermen, shepherds, teachers, etc.? It's not like it has any *name* writers who are well-known in Evangelical circles for lectures, preaching, direct mail campaigns, or radio and television talk shows.

And we Evangelical Christian readers are particularly uninspired to read unless the book has an accompaning study guide, cassette, traditional alliterated sub-headings, catchy book or chapter titles, and illustrations.

There are serious problems throughout the Bible with the characters, as well. Most of the good guys have serious flaws like lying, cheating, murder, adultery, incest and – frankly – I doubt if readers would accept it. We Evangelical readers want the good guys to be role-models for our entire families. What kinds of role models are these guys? One guy lied about his wife, said she was his sister and nearly married her off to another man. Then there was some long-haired tower of strength who disobeyed his parents, married a 'foreigner', got his hair cut and had his eyes put out. Then there was the king who murdered the husband of the woman he committed adultery with. Need I go on? What self-respecting parents would want to introduce their children to these 'men of God'?

The violence is extreme in places. Not just the usual shoot-outs, stabbings or karate chops. This contains decapitations, disembowelling, crucifixions, and lower intestinal worms.

There's the rampant sex to consider as well. Promiscuous heterosexuality, homosexuality, incest, etc. Some Evangelical men might sneak a peek like they do with the lingerie sections in a fashion catalog, but no one would actually *buy* a book with so many blatant goings-on.

What chance do we imagine we'd have with our little book?

The truth is: if I were a reviewer for a Christian publishing house and had to make a recommendation about this project, I'd advise them to forget it and publish *Ten Steps To Relaxing Without Feeling Guilty* instead.

So if we get a publisher who'll even consider an advance – yes, you'll get half.

But you never answered my question about Evangelicals, etc., in your country.

Tag. You're it.

21 July

Dear Brad

Where is my hostage, you cheat? I expected five lines about publishing in America and three pages on how you became a Christian. Tap out your testimony, Bradley, or the next one contains a bomb.

Yours disgustedly,

George

Dear George

All right already, don't get knots in your knickers – or whatever the expression is. I wasn't avoiding your request for my 'testimony' on purpose. I just got carried away talking about Christian publishing.

My testimony is pretty mundane stuff, really. My mother insisted that we go to church and we did every Sunday morning. Which church we went to depended on whether or not my mom was offended by something like the preacher being too long-winded, or people not eating all of her angel food cake at the church potluck, or whatever. In which case we jumped around from church to church, denomination to denomination. Methodist, Presbyterian, Baptist – we were all over the place. I got the basics through Sunday School. We colored pictures of Jesus holding little children or made little 'Bibles' out of a bar of soap sandwiched between two pieces of cardboard and sang 'Do Lord' and 'Jesus loves Me' and learned John 3:16 by heart. At home we said the 'Now I lay me down to sleep' prayer ever night at bedtime. It was all very simple. I never doubted that God listened or that he cared about me. Besides, I was a good boy and didn't see any reason *not* to believe.

So it didn't feel like a giant leap of faith when, at the age of ten, I was so moved by the story of the crucifixion – that Jesus died for *me* – that I asked him to forgive me and come into my heart. I'm sorry I don't have an exact date for that occurrence. In this country, it's a big thing to have a spiritual birthday. I don't know when it happened. I was alone in my room and don't think I told anyone for a few days after that. Nobody thought to mark the calendar.

When I finally told my mom, though, it was big news. I had to go forward during the 'altar call' (or 'invitation') at the next church service and the pastor made me stand in front of the whole church. The following Sunday I got baptized by full dunking. I enjoyed all the attention so much that the Sunday after *that* I went forward again and said I thought God was calling me into the ministry. All at the age of ten. Everyone was thrilled, especially my mom. To this day she waits for me to make good on that promise (writing doesn't count as a ministry, you see, you have to be a *pulpit-pounding* preacher). Good old Mom.

That's about it. Of course, there's a lot that happened later, but consider that another story for another time. You wanted to know how I met Jesus and that's it. Any questions?

I joined a new Bible study group, by the way.

Now, back to work. My editor's waiting; we have deadlines to meet. As always . . .

Tag. You're it.

Brad

6 *August*

Dear Bradley

The expression to which you refer is 'don't get your knickers in a twist',[1] and I didn't. I just wanted you to offer me some miserly fragment of yourself, and now that you have done so (offered me a miserly fragment, I mean), I've put the bomb on ice – for the time being anyway. I like the sound of your mother. Why don't you mention your father at all? Incidentally, if you think that this relatively brief piece of personal revelation entitles you to return for ever to your habit of skating briskly over every patch of thin ice in your life – well, think again! There's a lot more I want to know about you, Bradley Miller.

Incidentally, I hope you haven't set this 'getting published' vehicle rolling too far along the road towards actually going into print. I felt quite intimidated when I sat down to begin this letter. Are thousands of people really going to be fascinated to hear that I haven't got my knickers in a twist? I doubt it, somehow. Don't make any deals without letting me know, will you? If I find you've been having three-hour dinners with fat publishers on the basis of what this dumb cluck in England is going to write, I shall show you where the crayfish spend the winter, as the Russians so vividly put it. My usual output consists of bad poetry and editorials nowadays, so I'm not at all confident that I'll have much to offer. Endearingly self-effacing, though, don't you think?

Your news that you've joined a new Bible study group doesn't surprise me at all. You've yellow-bellied out, haven't you, Bradley, my chicken? Let's face it, you either had to let the members of the old group see the paragraph with your quote in it from my last letter but two, or leave. You did the sensible thing, Brad. I'd have done the same. You must tell me more about this new group. Do they sit around miserably discussing the theory of joy?

By the way, I ought to tell you that I actually became a Christian when I was sixteen after going to what seemed like one of the deadliest Bible study groups in the history of the Church. It was held in a friendly little tomb just down the road from me, and I only went the first time because the girl next door, who was very pretty and called Julia if I remember rightly, asked me if I'd like to join her and go to one of their meetings on the Thursday evening.

I only thought she was asking me out, didn't I Bradley? She had one of those smiles that made you just want to climb up inside it and go to sleep all warm and safe, and the kind of figure that made you hope she'd join you – wherever you ended up sleeping. As far as I can recall, the conversation (which makes me blush whenever I think of it) was conducted over the garden fence and went something like this:

Julia: Do you ever do anything on a Thursday evening?

Me: (*Knowing that I would have cancelled my mother's funeral if it meant going somewhere with this angel, but trying to sound as if life was one big fight to resist pressure to bestow my fascinating presence on every home in the neighbourhood*) Thursdays? Well, usually, yes, but I don't have to – I mean, whatever I might have on can always be changed if, if there's a reason to change it. I mean, if something came along that was a good reason to change whatever I had been going to do, then I would change it, if it was a good enough er . . . reason. Oh, yes, that would be no problem – to do that. To change it, I mean.

Julia: What about this Thursday?

Me: (*Pursing my lips and sucking in air as I flick through an* *imaginary mental engagement book*) Mmmm, let me see, no I don't think I've actually got anything planned for this Thursday, so I suppose – in that sense – it's free. (*I laugh too loudly and for too long, like a hyena being garrotted, as though I'd perpetrated some hilarious witticism.*)

Julia: (*Smiling, and turning me from a hyena into a little doggie who wants to do somersaults and stand on his hind legs just to please his mistress. Aaah, his mistress!*) Would you be interested in coming to a group I go to on Thursdays? It is a church group, though. I wouldn't want you to come along thinking it's something else.

Me: (*Filled with joy at the idea that this vision should want me to come along and listen to a music group with her. Never mind how pathetic the band might turn out to be. She wanted me to go with her! I was in love – again.*) Sounds great. When – how?

Julia: I'll call for you just before 7.30 – okay?

Me: (*Making a strange nasally affirmative grunting sound caused by joy and nerves meeting at the same time and place in my nose*) Nnn . . .

I feel very sorry for the sixteen-year-old lad that I was on that following Thursday evening, Bradley. I was sadly mistaken on two very important counts. First, I thought that Julia fancied me – how on earth could I have thought that? Why in this world would a girl like that be pursuing a skinny, spotty herbert like me? I must have been mad. Secondly, I thought we were going to listen to some crumby music group made up of selfish lead guitarist, incompetent rhythm guitarist, musically illiterate bass guitarist and unco-ordinated drummer. All the groups were like that in the sixties. I had this idea in my head that, after we'd endured an hour or so of bad music, I'd suggest we went down the Wimpy[2] (we're talking pre-McDonald's here, Bradley) and just gaze into each other's eyes over a burger and a frothy coffee for an hour or two. Then I'd walk her home and, by then, she'd be so overcome by my manly charm that she'd melt in my arms and give me one of them kisses what James Bond always got in the pictures.

Oh, Bradley, you should have seen me in the bathroom at seven o'clock that evening. I was washing and teeth-cleaning and spot-disguising and hair-combing (I'd had a Beatle-cut and my hair looked like a bad wig) and singing away like a little lark because I'd got a date with a beautiful girl, and I didn't have to worry about whether she really wanted to go because it was her who'd asked me. SHE HAD ASKED ME! I was so happy I thought I was going to burst. By 7.25 I was down by the front door, dressed up in my very best groovy gear, stinking wonderfully of cheap deodorant (she'd never be able to resist that) and checking my hair from every possible angle in the hall mirror as I waited for the two-tone doorbell to tell me that my dream-girl had arrived.

Bradley, she came with her boyfriend.

When I opened the door and flashed what I hoped was a winning smile at 'my' date, she said, 'George , this is my boyfriend, Vince, he's leading the prayers tonight.'

I hardly registered the bit about the prayers. First I had to control my face, and after that all I could see was bloody Vince, with his perfect bloody smile, his perfect bloody body, and his perfect, effortlessly casual but stylish bloody clothes. The rat even looked as if he might be nice as well! Add all that to the fact that he was called Vince, a useful name to have around that time, and you ended up with the kind of boyfriend that I hadn't been able to believe Julia was prepared not to have if she went out with me, if you see what I mean. How I managed to walk down that road with them I just don't know. I can remember feeling crumpled inside and wanting to cry because my dream was all smashed up and spoiled, but I didn't want them to know that, so I was trying to act cool and confident. I fantasized about killing bloody Vince and weeping all over Julia.

33   When we got to this house down the road and I discovered

I was at some sort of stupid Christian get-together, well, that really made my day, I can tell you, Bradley. What an intense joy it was to lose a beautiful girlfriend and gain a bunch of loonies.

Cherry's calling, Brad, so I'll have to go.

The end of the story is that I became a Christian that night.

George

Notes

[1] 'Knickers in a twist' = get unduly upset.

[2] Wimpy is a chain of fast-food hamburger restaurants, supposedly named after the character from the *Popeye* cartoon series.

August 11th

Dear George

What?!?!? I can't believe you dropped me in the middle of your conversion in order to tend to Cherry. I mean, I'm sure she's a wonderful little girl and feeding her dinner or reading her a story or putting her to bed is a delightful experience for both of you – but how did you get from your *non*-relationship with Julia (thanks to bloody Vince) and *into* a relationship with Jesus?

Tag. You're most *definitely* it.

Brad

P.S. I'd appreciate your prayers for my mom. She's had a relapse of her cancer. She had treatments for it a couple of years ago and we thought it had gone into complete remission. Wishful thinking. It's back and the doctors are trying to decide what to do.

18 *August*

Those who have never had children are in one giant
conceptual vacuum when it comes to trying to understand
the lives of those who have. Let me give you two examples of
the sort of thing we parents have to endure.

The first incident occurred when Cherry was quite a bit
younger. The phone went when I was seriously occupied in
the lavatory, and Cherry, who rather fancied herself (and still
does) as my personal and private secretary, picked it up and
said, exactly as I've taught her to, 'This is Cherry Smith here,
did you want to speak to my daddy?' There was a short pause
while the person on the other end said something, and then I
heard Cherry say, in her crystal-clear little voice, 'He won't be
long, he's just wiping his bottom, then he'll wash his hands,
and then he'll be able to speak to you.' I really, really didn't
want to pursue that call, but I did (after washing my hands, of
course). It was a girl from the dry cleaners in the shopping
precinct to tell me my suit was ready for collection. I had to
go in there that same day. I tell you, Bob Hope never got a
reception like I got in the dry cleaners that day. Brad, they
gave me a round of applause.

The other jolly little incident happened when my mobile
embarrassment machine was three years old. The new curate
(assistant pastor?) came with his wife to join me for Sunday
lunch. He was a young, very dignified, rather pink young man,
whose every body movement was self-consciously
spasmodic, and she was one of those people who seemed to
be physically bowed with devoutness. Conversation was so

stuffy that, by the time we got to the coffee stage, I felt as if all my internal organs were lodged in my throat. I wanted to die.

During a lull in the tortuous interchange, Cherry, who had recently been learning about the difference between men and women and the way in which people grow as they get older, leaned across towards the curate, clearly feeling that it was up to her, as hostess, to initiate a fresh topic of conversation. 'How big is your penis?' she enquired politely, in exactly the tone one might use to chat about the weather.

Oh, Bradley, it was wonderful. I have never seen a man go that colour before in my life, and I don't think I ever shall again. So much blood rushed to his head that he looked like a giant red tadpole. When he spoke he'd turned into a frog. 'Do I have to answer that?' he croaked. Luckily I was able to distract Cherry almost immediately (it had been an entirely innocent question) but I shall always be grateful to her for allowing me to witness, first hand, the effect of saying the precise thing that one would never choose as a topic of conversation over Sunday lunch with a visiting member of the clergy.

I love that girl.

Anyway, I only told you those two stories to show why I rushed off and cut short my story when Cherry called. You never, never know . . .

So, if you insist, back to my 'testimony'.

When I got into this drab little house with Julia and Vince they ushered me into the front sitting-room where I found seven or eight people sitting in a circle around the edge of the room, all holding Bibles and smiling broadly at me as if we'd known each other for years. Apparently they were members of the local parish church who were 'seeking God in new ways', whatever that meant. I really panicked for a moment. The sudden shift of emphasis from sex to religious mania was turning me inside out, but when I attempted a vague side-step towards the door the beautiful Julia took my arm and flashed one of those blasted smiles of hers at me and I was lost. She led me to a ludicrously small wooden chair in the corner and there I sat, dressed for a night out on the town, wishing I had a machine-gun in my hands and wanting – all right, I'll be honest Bradley – I wanted my mummy.

I can't remember much else about the first part of the meeting. I do recall that everybody seemed to be oddly excited, in a contained sort of way, about me being there because they kept nodding and grinning at each other, as if they knew something I didn't. And I remember thinking they seemed a dreary little crew on the whole. None of the women had nice legs (except Julia, and that no longer counted because I wasn't bloody Vince, damn his eyes) and the men looked sort of mild, with little good-natured tents of skin over their eyes. Funny what stays in your memory, isn't it?

It wasn't until the prayer-time that anything happened for me. Vince started the prayers, leaning forward with his arms on his knees, hands clasped together, his eyes screwed shut as he went into concentrated God-addressing mode. I was struck, I have to admit, by the *ordinary* way he talked to God, as if he really knew him, but that just confirmed my growing conviction that the men in white coats would be along to pick this lot up at any moment. There was absolutely no doubt in my mind, as I listened to some of the others praying, that these people were several degrees short of a right angle.

Then Julia prayed.

Bradley, it wasn't just that she was beautiful, although she was, and it wasn't just that she sounded warm and loved and loving, although she did. It was something that happened in me while she was speaking. I was still feeling very wobbly anyway after the Vince shock, so maybe that just made me more receptive – I'm not sure. I started to cry. Real tears. Running down your face sort of tears. No noise, just tears. Sadness and silliness and self-hate; wanting and not having and being disappointed; inside greyness and puzzled lines between the eyes; the shock of not being a child any more, of

38

knowing that there aren't really any grown-ups; hurt given and received – all those things flowing silently down. Then I began to talk. It was like a baby inside me reaching out his arms to someone who would understand – just baby-talk. Julia told me afterwards it was called 'speaking in tongues', but I didn't care what it was called. It was wonderful. Julia and bloody Vince explained a lot of things to me that night, and before I went home I'd made some kind of commitment. I was a Christian.

I spoke in tongues for years after that, but I haven't done it for a long time now and I'm not sure that I ever will again, Bradley, it was a wonderful gift, though – the first thing to bring me out of myself.

That's enough, I think.

George

P.S. Would you like to see some of the awful poetry I get sent? It is truly dreadful – I think you'd appreciate it. Is that an insult? I hope so.

August 28th

Dear George

Let me say right up front that these letters will have to be edited. I mean, if there was any doubt before, there isn't now. No chance *any* self-respecting Christian publisher will leave in your conversation with Cherry about . . . well, those things you talked about.

Thank you for finishing your testimony. It resonated within my own experience for a couple of different reasons. This whole thing about speaking in tongues has always been a curiosity to me. It still is. Timely that you'd mention it now in light of something that recently happened to me. It's all connected to the Bible study group I mentioned. It has a member who's into things like speaking in tongues, but I'll tell you about her in a minute.

The Bible study itself is supposed to be a discussion group about basic Christianity, but some of us secretly call it 'Christians Anonymous'. That's mostly because Dave, the leader of the group, treats our meetings like group therapy. No matter what the subject Dave insists that we 'share our feelings'. Frankly, I'm not sure how I'm supposed to 'feel' about translations of the Bible or plumbing fixtures used for baptism in the first century. More often than not, I find I have to make up some feelings just so he'll leave me alone.

I hesitantly mentioned my prayer request for my mom. The doctors have put her back on chemo. I know she's miserable from the side-effects. But she's a tough woman and tries not to show how much it affects her.

There are only a handful of us in the group, but we're

diverse. I'll tell you about everyone some other time. The only one worth mentioning for the moment is Diane. She's fervently spiritual in everything she does. She speaks fervently, prays fervently, cries fervently, even smiles fervently. Maybe it's because she teaches first grade at the David and Goliath Day Care and Whole Armor of God Christian School.[1] Everyone thinks her fervency makes her seem closer to God. I think it makes her kind of sexy. That, and her fervent blonde hair and remarkable dimples.

I told her about our correspondence. I thought she'd be helpful in our research, and your discussion of speaking in tongues seemed a natural link. Besides, I wanted to impress her with my international connections. And she was, too. She asked me to give her a lift home after last week's meeting so we could talk about it. Of course I played hard-to-get and agreed only after a very long millisecond.

As we drove, she explained why she was so confident that the Lord would heal my mother. She said she'd seen a lot of healing in her life – she almost made it sound commonplace. Bad backs, allergies, ingrown toenails, and one remarkable story about a man who had been born with one leg shorter than the other and how they miraculously prayed them to equal proportions. All because they believed. According to Diane, healing is only a mustard-seed of faith away.

It sounded so reasonable and Diane was so earnest (and so incredibly cuddly-looking in that particular sweater) that I agreed whole-heartedly with everything she said – even though I didn't know a thing about it. I eventually and reluctantly confessed my confusion.

Diane was . . . well, fervent. 'Once I was filled with the Spirit and felt his power – there was nothing left to be confused about. Everything became clear. I believe any confusion about our Christianity is the result of denying the Spirit access into our modern lives,' she declared.

Ah! You have an ally, George.

We reached her apartment where she made some tea. After

my second cup, I asked her what brand it was. 'Bless You,' she said. I thanked her and asked again what brand of tea it was. 'Bless You,' she repeated. 'My favorite.' I didn't understand. She informed me that the Lipton company started a Christian line of tea. 'Bless You Tea . . . Heavenly Irish Breakfast . . . Praise Pekoe is a favorite,' she smiled, then got straight to business.

'How can God give us his ongoing revelation if we box him into worn-out ideas and traditions?' she asked, clearly knowing the answer personally. 'Worship, for example.' I sat down on a bean-bag chair as she pulled an old hymnal from her stacked-to-the-point-of-sagging bookshelves. They weren't sagging because of books, but thanks to a burden of Christian plaques and pictures of kittens that said things like 'Happiness is . . . to know Jesus' and 'To Know Him is to Love Him'. She continued, 'I was looking through this old hymnal. Some of this stuff is okay, I guess. Listen . . .' She opened to a page and began to read:

'A mighty fortress is our God, a bulwark never failing
Our helper he amid the flood of mortal ills prevailing
For still our ancient foe, doth seek to work us woe
His craft and pow'r are great,
      and armed with cruel hate
On earth is not his equal.'

I nodded, not knowing what her point was.

'Seriously now. I understand the mighty fortress part, but who knows what a bulwark is? Sounds like a bird. I'm sure they were good lyrics for their time, but – now? Have you ever tried to wave your arms in the air to a song like this?'

I didn't dare tell her that I wasn't inclined to wave my arms to *any* song. It's a flaw, I know.

'I have some lyrics to a little chorus I wrote. Do you want to hear them?' Diane carefully unfolded a piece of paper from her handbag.

Was I going to say no?

'Here they are,' she said, and began to sing a song. Each verse was directed to the Father, Son and Spirit respectively in which we praised them, worshiped them, loved them, served them, respected them, anticipated them, held fast to them, had peace with them, had joy with them, and . . .

Well, you get the idea. If I'd worked it out with a calculator her 'little chorus' would have had 114 verses, not including the bridge and orchestral interlude.

When she finished, she said, 'The Lord gave me those words last night while I was sleeping. Has that ever happened to you? It does when you're filled with the Spirit. I claimed them by faith. Don't you think they're better than bulwarks?'

I smiled non-committally – bulwarks weren't something I spent a lot of time thinking about.

'Have you been empowered by the Holy Spirit?' she asked.

I felt like I had been asked a trick question and struggled for the right answer. 'I . . . uh . . . well . . . thought the Holy Spirit came inside of me when I accepted Jesus,' I answered.

She knelt next to me and took my hand sympathetically (at which point I probably would've accepted *anything*). She smiled and said, 'Let's pray for the Holy Spirit to come into you *now*,' and then began to pray right then and there for the Spirit to come upon me so I could experience his fullness. I was so surprised that I began to stammer that I wasn't sure I was ready for such a thing. Of course, the stammering obliterated my sentence structure so much that she became ecstatic that I'd received the gift of tongues so quickly. What could I do? I may be a letch, but I'm not a fraud. I confessed immediately that I *wasn't* speaking in tongues and didn't even know where to begin.

She patiently explained – still holding my hand – that I simply needed to 'let go' of myself and say the words 'Thank you, Jesus, praise you, Jesus' over and over. I sighed deeply and tried to decide if I could 'let go' of all my years of non-Charismatic teaching (including a short stint in Bible college) to 'let go' of myself. I thought it was worth trying. But the thing I needed to 'let go' of wasn't myself, but her *hand* so I could pray sincerely without distraction.

And pray I did – getting more and more enthusiastic, even downright *fervent* – building to a crescendo that sounded less and less like prayer and more like begging, pleading and cajoling. Nothing happened. We tried again. The same result. I collapsed in a puddle of sweat.

Diane looked at me with a mixed expression of disappointment and accusation. 'Are you *sure* you're a Christian?' she asked.

I shrugged, 'I thought so . . . until now.'

It was obvious to both of us that there was nothing left to be done for the moment and I went home. She said she wanted to see me again – apart from the Bible study – but after showing myself to be such a spiritual failure, I wasn't sure why.

So there you have it. My first big experience in the land of the gifted.

You said you don't speak in tongues anymore. What happened? Did you decide not to or did you lose it, or did God take his gift back? I don't understand how it works.

Brad

P.S. I'm not much of a poetry reader but would love to see the kind of stuff you're writing or editing, or whatever it is you do with it.

Notes
[1] This really is the name of the school.

6 September

In view of your carnal attitude to Devout Diane, I would suggest that the less you think about tongues the better. As for the laying on of hands – forget it. Honestly, how on earth did you expect to share the contents of her heart when all you could think about was the contents of her jumper?[1] (We don't say the word 'sweater' – that word describes you in the presence of D.D.) I can tell you from personal experience that you need a bloody Vince to pour cold water over nine parts of you, so that the tenth and spiritual part is left with elbow room to operate. Seriously, Dusty, how – or why – did you let yourself get into a situation like that? – if you really did. When you launch into this short-story mode of yours I can't tell if you're writing it the way it was, with a spot of embroidery, or setting yourself up as the next great Christian satirist. Having said that, I do think that this particular little tale must have some basis in truth, mainly because of the 'puddle of sweat'. Also, beneath the shimmering symptoms of our common textually communicated disease, I do seem to detect the leaden reality of a genuine sense of failure.

I don't want to be too sympathetic in case it was all a load of rubbish, but I do want to say that if you challenge me to use the gift of tongues again I'll have a go – if you do as well. Here's the deal (that's good Americanese, isn't it?). You find someone with more spiritual wisdom than chest and ask if *he* will pray with you at a time that we'll co-ordinate in advance. I'll pray as well, and then we shall see what we shall see. Let me know if you want to do this because I'll have to let God know in time for the dusty old George Smith file to be dragged off the 'pending' shelf and read through by whichever angel is on my case.

In the meantime, you said you'd be interested to see some of the poems that I get sent by hopefuls for inclusion in my magazine. The vast majority of them are mind-bogglingly bad, but every now and then something interesting comes along. Here's a piece I got the other day from an anonymous contributor in the south somewhere. It certainly couldn't be classified as poetry, but in view of the current debate about hell in this country (not worth debating over there under your present administration, I guess) I found it quite stimulating. Read it and tell me what America thinks about hell – not an amusing little anecdote about what happened when you visited the devil for a weekend.

I'm in hell with some angry people
The atheists say it's a crime
They say they'll endeavour
For ever and ever
To prove they were right all the time.

I'm in hell with some rueful people
False prophets are microwaved whole
And the folks that they led
To this land of the dead
Are in charge of the heating control.

I'm in hell with some churchgoing people
Whose groups were in conflict I fear
They've given up hate
But now it's too late
They're eternally unified here.

I'm in hell with some reverend people
Including a bishop or three
Each turns on his spit

And the heat's not a bit
Less liberal than they used to be.

I'm in hell with some ordinary people
There's a man who while living in Slough
Was a barbecue freak
He had three every week
So he's right in his element now.

I'm in hell with some literate people
The books that they've read – what a list!
They were frequently lost in
Camus and Jane Austen
But could there be something they missed?

I'm in hell with some well-travelled people
They rambled in Dorset and Devon
They drove and they flew
From Algiers to Peru
But they can't find a way into heaven.

I'm in hell with some sporty people
A Wimbledon player said, 'Why,
When these others have earned
The right to be burned
Have I been put through on a bye?'

I'm damned with available women
Of every complexion and size
I'd like to cash in
On the wages of sin
But I can't face the hell in their eyes.

I'm here with some wonderful people
We all know we're guiltless as well
It seems such a shame
When no one's to blame
That we're all as unhappy as hell.

I'm in hell with some lovely people
But I think we're beginning to peel
There are bits dropping off
When we stumble and cough
And wherever we touch we congeal.[2]

Tasteless, eh? Well, it would be over here. Hell is not nearly as important to the Church in England as it seemed to be to Jesus. Americans seem to think they're going to live for ever anyway, so perhaps eternal punishment's just not relevant to you lot. True? Spill it, Dusty!

Yours,

George

P.S. Your mum's illness is making my stomach churn and my heart ache. I want to be able to pray for her but every time I try, someone else's face comes into my mind and I have to clench my teeth to hold the raging in. Damn you, Dusty, I never wanted to be resurrected again.

P.P.S. Show your mum the poem about hell – tell her that anyone who's put up with you for nearly thirty years has got to have something good lined up for her. Give her my love.

Notes
[1] Jumper = sweater.

[2] We did our very best to find out who wrote this interesting little poem. George claims that he has lost all paperwork related to it. We suspect that the author of the poem is, in fact, George himself. This poses an interesting contradiction since George laments that people in Britain are reticent about discussing hell, then refuses to take credit (or blame) for a poem about the same subject.

Dear George

I'm rushing off to my study group (read: Christians
Anonymous) but wanted to get this in the mail to you on the
way.

First, what's with calling me 'Dusty'? I thought at first you
had sent me a letter you meant for someone else, until I saw
the references to 'Devout Diane'. Please explain.

About 'Devout Diane'. Granted, it wasn't the most sensible
way to start a spiritual encounter, but *you* became a Christian
following your devious hopes for Julia, so don't get on your
high horse about what happened to me. It *did* happen, by the
way. I promise, if I'm going to include any more fictional
encounters I'll say so in advance. Okay? (And I *never* said
anything about anybody's *chest*, you pervert.)

I'm not sure I'm ready to make any deals about speaking in
tongues. I'd like to know why you stopped, but I wouldn't
insist that either one of us do it. My Bible college teaching
says they were dispensed with after the first century anyway.
I'm not sure I agree with that, but I don't know that we want
to spend the time discussing it here. And, frankly, I doubt if
it'll make a difference if I pray with Diane or Donald or Daffy
Duck – I'm not keen to get myself all worked up over a gift
God may not want me to have. 'Not *all* speak in tongues, do
they?' the Apostle Paul wrote somewhere.

Thanks for the poem about hell. I thought it was very funny.
I should've added hell to the list when discussing the
differences between Conservatives and Liberals in this
country. Conservatives believe in it because a righteous God

can't allow those who don't know Jesus into heaven. The Liberals don't believe in it because they can't reconcile it with the idea of God being all-loving.

I believe in it because I was once a youth leader.

Again, you mentioned the Church in England without giving me a clue about what that is. Is the Church *in* England the same as the Church *of* England and the same as the Anglican Church?

I'm hesitant to ask why my mom's illness is affecting you the way it is. Whose face do you see? Tell me only when you're ready. But that P.S. was enough to get my mother and me to pray for *you*. She also decided after your P.P.S. that she likes you.

Give Cherry a big hello from me. Do you have a picture of the two of you?

So much for a *quick* letter. I may write another later tonight after the study group. I think I'm going to ask Diane out on a proper date (just keep your comments to yourself).

Brad

September 12th

Dear George

It's later now – same day as the letter you'll probably get the day before this one. I hope this doesn't throw our order out of whack.

You'll be interested to know that, after tonight's meeting, I asked Diane if we could have dinner together. She told me that she thought it would be best if we didn't 'get involved like that' since we're both in the same study group and it'll complicate things if it doesn't work out. How thoughtful of her to think it through so carefully – and so quickly. Or did she have a prophetic word before I asked her?

I didn't finish telling you about the other members of our study group and probably should since these letters and they are now intertwined (an explanation in a minute). I told you about Diane, of course. I think I also told you about Dave, who treats the group like we're all in therapy. He has a very smooth 'get it all out in the open' kind of style. I used to appreciate that approach, but now it makes me nervous. Carl is a middle-aged sales representative with the phone company. He's our resident Conservative theologian. Dave once said that Carl's theology was as systematic as a telephone system – and worked about as well, too. We laughed. Carl said he didn't understand the humor of the statement. Then there's Karen. She's rather sweet and mousy and hangs onto her Bible like a life preserver. It's covered with colorful stickers and clever slogans – the kind that are supposed to catch your eye and lead you to a knowledge of the goodness and love of God in five words or less. And finally there's Ruth. She's very down-to-earth, sturdy. She's a career girl who occasionally requests prayer about the lack of a 'love life' in her life. I'm not sure why she'd have a problem in that area. I mean, she's not a knock-out, but she isn't unattractive either. And I admire her character. If I had a problem, Ruth's the one I'd talk to.

I'm telling you all this because the meeting took a peculiar turn and I think it might interest you since we're trying to do those articles. For reasons of her own, Diane announced to everyone that you and I were corresponding about what it is to be a Christian in our respective countries (not an accurate description, but close enough). This led Dave to want to 'explore' the idea with our little group. He decided everyone should answer the questions: Who *are* you as a Christian? How do you see yourself? How do others see you?

No one dared to speak.

Dave bravely pressed onward, 'You see, I'm a Christian because, for me, Christianity *works*. It works for *me*, and – '

'Works?' Carl interrupted. '*Grace*, my friend.'

Dave said he didn't want to quibble. Carl began to quibble about whether it was quibbling to quibble. Dave said he didn't want to get lost in semantics. Carl accused Dave of being anti-semantic, then realized what he said and blushed. Dave told Carl to shut up, in Christian love, and proceeded with the meeting.

'Who are we?' he asked.

Again no one spoke.

Dave told us it was easy. 'I want each of you to say your name and then tell us how you see yourself as a Christian. Okay?'

Now you see why we call it Christians Anonymous, George.

Dave called on Carl first. Carl considered the idea and said his name was Carl and that he was 'free in Christ'. Dave made us applaud, then turned to Diane. With great fervency, she said, 'I'm Diane and I'm just a small temple to house the

Lord's spirit!' More applause. Karen announced that she 'wasn't perfect, just forgiven!' And when everyone applauded, she seemed to feel encouraged enough to add: 'Wise men still seek him!'

Dave gestured to Ruth and she blushed furiously. 'I'm Ruth and I'm . . . I'm . . .' She didn't have an answer and I was both uncomfortable for her and grateful. I didn't know what I was going to say either. Dave egged her on. 'I'm working on it,' Ruth snapped. Everyone applauded until we realized that she hadn't answered the question, but meant she was still working on the answer. Dave implored her to come up with something.

Diane tried to encourage her. 'Just say, "I'm Ruth" and then fill in the blank.'

'I'm Ruth and . . . I'm . . . I'm confused,' she said, trying to put an end to it. Dave wouldn't leave it alone and said we'd stay all night until she came up with an answer of some sort. 'I'm just being honest,' Ruth finally said. 'I've been thinking about it and . . . it's hard to figure out. In the world and not of it . . . and all that stuff. I don't get it.' She looked around the room. 'I'm sorry. I'm a Christian, but it's hard to know what that really means.'

Karen reached over and took Ruth's hand meaningfully.

'I think we have our work cut out for us,' Dave said and told us to open our Bibles. I was relieved. Dave forgot about me.

I talked to Ruth during our coffee break. I confessed quietly that I understood how she felt. She shrugged, 'I could have lied. That's always been the easiest thing to do. As long as I'm behaving properly, going to church, teaching Sunday School, participating in socially acceptable activities with my Christian friends, nobody needs to know what's going on inside of me. I'm accepted. What's there to be confused about? It's us against the world. Simple, right?'

I didn't answer.

She continued, 'But the world I'm supposed to be against is the one I live in. It's full of my friends who *aren't* Christians.

People I care about. Oh, they respect my beliefs . . . as long as I don't bring them up. That suits me. They would only feel uncomfortable if I tried to explain – and they wouldn't understand anyway. So I'm accepted. In both groups. In both worlds. But never at the same time.'

Again, I assured her that I understood how she felt.

She shrugged again, 'I'm just trying to be honest. I mean, I look around at other Christians and . . . sometimes I think we're just plain weird.'

How could I argue?

Brad

September 29th

I haven't heard from you in awhile. Should I be concerned?
Tag. You're still it.

Brad

3 *October*

Dear Bradley

The 'Dusty' was just to confuse you. In England, people with the surname Miller are sometimes nicknamed Dusty, presumably because, in the old days, when the name reflected the trade, your ancestors would have spent most of the working day with their heads in a sort of white cloud. And you, Bradley Miller, seem to be carrying on the family tradition to this very day. Have you any idea what it cost me to suggest that we to go God for something at the same time, and particularly something like the gift of tongues, which meant everything to me when I first met Jesus, you pillock!?!

As for trotting out the old 'Not all speak in tongues, do they?' verse – I'm amazed that you dare cower behind that old chestnut. Has it not occurred to you that, whilst implying many people don't speak in tongues, it also makes it quite clear that an awful lot do?

And what's this flip phrase '. . . the Apostle Paul wrote somewhere'? What do you mean 'somewhere'? W*here* did he write it, Bradley? On the back of a cigarette packet, do you think? Or in the introduction to the Jewish Sanitary Inspector's handbook, perhaps? Maybe he scratched it on the wall of the gent's toilet in Ephesus under 'Kilroy wos converted 'ere'. Didn't the same Bible college that so casually dismissed my trivial little life-changing experience teach you where to find the verse that you use to squelch the first fragment of spiritual vulnerability I've shown in years?

What is it with you, Bradley? Here are some possibilities:

(1) You're American and you don't know any better.

(2) You just want half a book out of me and it irritates you when I communicate on any other level than a purely superficial one.

(3) You're staggeringly shallow.

(4) (And this one's three lengths ahead and galloping past the winning post as far as I'm concerned) You don't dare to come out from behind that sardonic smugness of yours because you know damn well there are things you need to deal with and you're plain scared of showing or facing the feelings that are going to come out when you do.

You write very amusingly about the members of your study group, Brad, but it's easy to laugh at them. I suppose you had a good laugh at me too, did you, after you got my last letter?

I hope you get to heaven (soon) and find that God is Daffy Duck.

George

P.S. You're a coward, Bradley. You failed before, and you're frightened of failing again. Face it.

4 *October*

Dear Bradley

By now, I assume, you'll have read my last letter, written and posted yesterday just before midnight. I didn't sleep much after finally going to bed last night, mainly because I wished I could go and get that letter back from the dark and unregurgitating bowels of the post-box. This morning, after taking Cherry to school and before going off to do no work at the office, I turned the word-processor on and read what I'd written three or four times. I also read one or two of my previous effusions, just to see how they matched up. After a bit I couldn't face any more. So much anger and bitterness directed at you. Why? Such sarcasm and vitriol. What's the matter with me?

Now, I know what you're saying to yourself. Typical neurotic – first he's monumentally nasty to me and then I have to feel sorry for him because he's suddenly woken up to just how nasty he is. But I don't want you to feel sorry for me. Well, I do really, of course – but mainly I want to apologize for being so stupid. I'm sure that I've been dumping a lot of garbage on you that should really have been dumped on someone else. I won't tell you who the someone else is, but here's a cryptic clue: He created the world, but put nothing between Greenland and Denmark (three letters). Tricky, eh? Let me know if you don't get it, and I'll send you the answer. Forgive me. There's no excuse for being so abrasive. None of it is your problem. Since the British discovered emotions back in the sixties they have a tendency to drape their entrails over anyone who stands still for long enough, and, in my case, you were the only motionless human candidate.

I suppose there is a sliver of an excuse for losing my sense of judgement. Her name's Cherry. You wouldn't believe how complex the life of an English six-year-old girl is these days. By the end of yesterday I was driven to my knees by the weight of Cherry-related organization and activity. The fashion in this country at the moment is for small girls to be involved in a bewildering array of after-school activities, so that they have the opportunity to specialize later on. Cherry does dancing on Monday (tap, ballet and modern) immediately after school; followed by a session of unbelievable chaos at Squibs, the church-run kids' club; followed by television at home with me; followed by tea,[1] cooked and served by me; followed by a bath, run and supervised by me; followed by a story, read by me; followed by prayers, hypocritically insisted on by me; followed by attempts to prolong the day, resisted by me; followed by sleep, observed with relief by me.

The other days are more or less the same, except that the activities are different. Pot-holing, boxing, nuclear physics for under-sevens, sky-diving, tree-felling, sumo-wrestling, brick-laying, first level bunny-hops – might have got some of those wrong, but the list is endless. And every activity has to have its achievement certificates nowadays, so that the little dears never feel discouraged. The trouble is that ludicrously low levels of attainment are positively reinforced, as though it was Dr Skinner's pigeons learning to peck a green button rather than human children trying to grasp the first principles of air-combat, or whatever it is they're engaged in. Take swimming, for instance. Can it really be good for children to hear that they've been awarded the 'Woke-up-in-the-morning-thought-about-going-swimming-and-almost-did-but-turned-over-and-went-back-to-sleep-in-the-end' badge? That may be a slight exaggeration, but it is a real problem.

Cherry's had the best of me over the last two or three years, Bradley. I postpone my own gruesomeness when I'm with her, but it ain't half hard work sometimes. I have to role-play being the person I used to be and could, by a very optimistic assessment, become again one day. I can't bear the thought that her joy and innocence might be clouded by my moods and miseries, so I really do try very hard to be what she needs and wants in a father who has to be some kind of mother as well. With Cherry I'm bright! I joke! People who only know me as a puddle of gloom are amazed when they see me with my daughter. Like I said, I even insist on her saying her prayers every night. I quite often wonder how she'd react if she was with me and could see what a hypocrite I really am.

Here's a silly thing (and don't worry – I no longer expect you to cherish my fragile offerings as if they were your own little darling babies): When I take my shoes off at night – are you paying attention, Bradley? – I always want to kick them off without undoing the laces. And why shouldn't I? Now that I'm a grown man I can make big decisions like that. But I always, always painstakingly undo the laces, because two people are leaning invisibly over my shoulder, watching what I'm doing. One is Cherry, who gets told off by Daddy if she doesn't undo buckles or laces before putting on and taking off her shoes, and the other is Cherry's mummy, Gemma, who can't be with us any more but used to say to me just about every night, 'George, you're going to ruin those shoes – can't you undo them first?' It used to annoy me so much when she said that, but I'd give anything, *anything* to hear her say those words to me again. I want her with me to make everything feel all right, and I hate God for taking her away. I love him as well, but this is a long sulk.

Sorry to ramble so much. Feel quite free to send all your best bereavement-counselling jokes. I crave insensitivity. Beat Me! Beat me!

P.S. Give my love to the group, your mother, the President, Daffy Duck, and particularly to Devout Diane – she sounds like my kind of jumper.

P.P.S. Here is a solemn promise: in my very next letter the first thing I shall write about will be the Anglican Church, or Church of England. (I wonder what the difference is?)

Notes
[1] 'Tea', in this case, is an all-encompassing word for dinner or supper, not just the hot beverage.

October 10th

Dear George

I'm bewildered. I spent a couple of days at my mother's and got home to a stack of mail. I was surprised – after such a long silence – to find *two* letters from you. I wasn't paying enough attention when I opened them and wound up reading them in the wrong order.

It's probably providential that I did, because the second letter helped soften the blow of the first. I gratefully accept your apology in the second letter. But I can't let everything in the first letter slide without comment. A *very sincere* comment, if such a thing is possible for an American.

I am (1) and probably (4).

We Americans are curiously transparent in a superficial way. Just watch our talk shows and you'll see that Americans are willing to talk about *anything*. And we seem to do it without any suffering or pain. We've become emotional contortionists – able to turn ourselves inside out without stretching a muscle. So when I write to you about a personal experience, it's not surprising that you can't tell whether or not it really happened or I made it up. The tone is the same, I guess. At least, that's how it is with me (I won't speak for all Americans). Make light of it, find a clever phrase, write it off with a joke or a flippant remark . . . that's how I cope. That's how I've *always* coped. It may offend your British sensibilities, but how could I possibly know that until now? And how do I change? When I don't mean to sound flippant, I sound flippant. I don't even hear it anymore, to know when I'm doing it.

Next point: Yeah – maybe I am giving the great *non-Charismatic* excuse about my failure to speak in tongues, hiding behind specific scripture, theology, etc. (Though I never imagined that quoting Paul *without* giving chapter and verse was so anathema to you. Yes, I went to Bible college, but that was eight years ago – and I've been trying to get over it ever since.) Regardless, I'm not ready to try again. There's too much happening in my life right now to complicate it with an experience that could yank my theological security blanket out of my hands.

Next point: You're also right when you say I have no idea *what* these letters are costing you. Obviously a lot. Why? It's a little clearer than it was, but not crystal-clear. And that's the problem. Forgive me for this, but you can't be let off the hook. You lashed out at me for being insensitive, superficial and scared – okay, I accept that. But it's unfair for you to chastise me, then offer only the tiniest crumbs of information about what has happened to you. I may be flippant, but, as you admitted, you're pretty good at using your *own* brand of British sarcasm like a blunt weapon to fight off *your* true feelings. I can't decipher your cryptic references to the things that hurt you in my letters. Pretend that I really am the idiot you think I am (easy to do). Can you tell me plainly just what in the world happened to you? . . . to Gemma? . . .

In other words: I'll come out if you'll come out (to use your own words). No pressure, though. Only when you're ready. (But I may have to resort to giving your address to Diane. She'll get the truth out of you one way or the other.)

And, for crying out loud, if you don't want to do the book, just say so. It isn't *that* important. As it is, Andy hasn't seen anything yet that he thinks is useable for an article *or* a book. The idea was never supposed to be a dentist's tool to poke and probe your exposed nerve. It was intended as a light-hearted look at the differences between our countries (Christianity-wise). If you *want* to do it, then fine. If not, forget about it.

All my love to Cherry. It sounds like she leads a very exciting life. Will you send me a picture?

Brad

P.S. What's a pillock? It sounds like a medicinal cushion.

15 *October*

Dear Brad

I flinched as I picked up your letter. I opened it with the tips
of my fingers and read it out of the corner of my eye. I so
hoped that, by some miracle, my letter before last might
have been lost in the post or abstracted by God before it got
to you. But it wasn't. I realized, too late, that the only way to
make absolutely sure of the letter's non-arrival would have
been to place a fortune-making bet on it reaching you.
However, I didn't, so it did. I can't blame you for your
reaction. Thank God I said I'd talk about the Church of
England before I did anything else. My grovelling is
postponed while I do so.

Here then is the answer to the question that has been
keeping you awake every night for months and months. The
Anglican Church is the worldwide communion of Anglicans,
and the Church of England is the English branch of the
Anglican communion, the whole thing presided over by the
Archbishop of Canterbury. Worth waiting for, eh?

I sometimes try to picture how it must be for a newly
appointed Archbishop to wake up on the first morning of his
appointment. As his vision clears, and his mind moves
sluggishly into gear, he mistily recalls that something has
happened, some quite significant change in his personal
circumstances. 'Good God!' he cries reverently, reaching over
to shake his wife's shoulder. 'Wake up, Bertha – I'm the
Archbishop of Canterbury!' How his wife copes with the
knowledge that she has just spent a night with the head of
the worldwide Church is totally unfathomable.

At least they wake up together. Imagine: 'Aaaaah – I'm the Pope!!'

I would hate to be leading the Anglican Church in this country at the moment, not least because it really is very difficult to know what it means to be a member of the Church of England any more. I could take you (if you were less interested in pubs than churches) to an Anglican church where the vicar is leading his people into Spirit-filled revival, and to another where God is regarded as a sort of amiable parish worker whose role is non-intrusive and politely uncritical at all times. An Anglican might be an atheist or a believer; a Charismatic or a conservative evangelical; a ceremonialist or a simple soul; he might attend a mass, or a eucharist, or a communion, or he might even gather around the Lord's table if enough folks have drifted across from some holy local shed where a split has occurred. Anglicans are strongly in favour of the ordination of women, and also strongly against it. The ordination of practising homosexuals is completely unacceptable, and, of course, totally acceptable as well. Anglicans are assured that Jesus died to save them from their sins, but they also believe that atonement is a peculiarly Jewish concept. The enthusiasm with which some Anglican churches reach out to meet social needs is matched only by the determination with which others do not. Not all of us are going to be saved and go to heaven, but, don't worry, we shall all be there.

I could go on and on, but I must stop to answer one question that you're probably not even asking: 'Why, in view of all this, is George Smith, famous for his wrinkled, prune-like faith, an Anglican?' The answer is that, at its best, the Church of England is wonderful. We have an event over here called the ARM Conference (ARM stands for Anglican Renewal Ministries). This gathering brings together a load of more or less weary clergymen and their wives to find a spot of refreshment, spiritual and social (there is a bar there), and to just be together. I'm not a clergyman, for which I fervently thank and praise His holy name, but I've been there. Mixing traditional depth and weight with the light and colour and exuberance of revival produces a most excellent soup. You must try it some time. What I am saying? I shall start praying if I'm not careful.

I hope that does happen.

Gemma died after a collision on the motorway.[1] I wasn't in the car. She lived for three days in dreadful pain, and died just after holding Cherry for the first time since the crash. I think that's as much as I can say for the moment.

As for the book – I dunno . . . It seems very unimportant somehow. If any of this is any use to anyone – why not? Who's this 'Andy', by the way?

George

P.S. Sorry/Sorry/Sorry/Sorry/Sorry/Sorry/Sorry/Sorry/Sorry.

P.P.S. I'll send you a picture of Cherry if you send me a picture of Devout Diane.

P.P.P.S. SORRY.

Notes
[1] A major roadway or freeway.

October 21st

Dear George

I'm glad you explained about Gemma. Thank you. You don't have to say anymore about it unless you really want to.

And thanks for the update on Anglicanism. Andy, the editor at the magazine I freelance for, liked it and thinks it should be the starting point for our series of articles.

Andy, by the way, is a nice guy, but considering he is the editor for *Today's Christian World*, he doesn't have a lot of patience with today's Christian world. And he tells a lot of corny jokes that most people heard and dispensed with when they were five years old. We don't have a large readership.

He (Andy) faxed me something he got off the International Christian News Wire. Apparently there's a move to start Christian radio stations in England. I take it from the article that there's some concern about what Christian radio in England would be like. Anything you might want to say on the subject would be helpful.

On the flip-side, I think it's worth letting you know what may be coming your way. Christians in America have a whole bunch of material they'll be happy to send over if you get on the air. In my town, we have a station called 'Love 81' – Blairville's 'favorite Christian station'. Actually, it's Blairville's *only* Christian radio station – buried deep in the static of an AM signal. After dusk it is overpowered by a rock music station broadcasting out of Bolivia. I know this only because I happen to like the station from Bolivia. It gives me the feeling of being an international sort of person to actually *hear* what's happening in another part of the world – even though I can't understand a word the disk jockey says.

Actually, I have to confess the same is sometimes true on the Christian station. For example, I was driving to work the other day and heard the following from one of the announcers:

'And our weather today looks like it's going to get just a little cooler than it was yesterday. You know, the weather changes every day but, you know, God doesn't change. Isn't that wonderful? He never changes. The weather does, but God doesn't. Isn't that exciting? God never changes. He stays the same. Even when the weather changes, God remains unchanging. He is constant, consistent, continual, regular, steady. He doesn't change. The weather does, you know, but He doesn't . . .'

And on and on. It reminded me of one of those children's rounds that you can't seem to stop singing once you start.

Do you have advertisements for contingency lawyers?' You will if you get Christian radio. You'll hear the sound of skidding tires and blaring horns, and then a friendly voice will ask, 'Have you been hurt in a car accident recently? Well, you may not know it, but you could be entitled to a monetary settlement for your medical expenses, time lost and inconvenience. Lipsynch, Wells and Forensics are Christian lawyers who will lovingly take your case to court.'

And then they'll explain how you'll get what you deserve while they'll get what *they* deserve for helping you get what you deserved. That's what a contingency lawyer does. Other ads come from insurance agents and counselors.

If your stations follow a music format, you'll get songs from groups like The Solid Rock Singers, The Cornerstone Singers, The Sonshine Singers, The King's Kids Singers, and The He-Is-The-Way-The-Truth-And-The-Life Singers. If your station goes for a 'rockier' sound, you'll get groups like Solid Rock, Cornerstone, Sonshine, King's Kids and He-Is-The-

Way-The-Truth-And-The-Life-And-Don't-You-Forget-It. If your station dares to play Heavy Metal Christian music, the groups will have names like Solid Rock In Your Face, Blood-Stained Cornerstone, Shattered Sonshine, King's Kids Who Wear Spandex And Yell 'Til The Veins Stand Out On Their Foreheads, and He-Is-The-Way-The-Truth-And-The-Life-Or-Burn-In-Hell.

Some Christian stations go with a talk show format, where believers get a full dose of practical help, inspiration and biblical learning through shows that candidly discuss things like 'Power for Living', 'Spiritual Strength through Controlled Perspiration', 'Hermeneutics and You', and 'Removing the Stain of Sin (and Spots of Gravy, too) from Your Life'. Families, housewives, career parents, single moms, single dads, single kids, teens, reformed teens, divorced parents, semi-divorced parents, divorced parent children of alcoholics . . . there's something for everyone.

You may think I'm joking about this, but I'm not. Well, mostly not. Consider yourself informed (warned).

Brad

P.S. No fair. I asked you for a picture of Cherry long before you ever heard about Diane. Besides, I don't think she'll give me one. And there's less of a chance she has one in that particular 'jumper' I mentioned, so don't get yourself all worked up.

Notes
[1] In America, 'contingency lawyers' are lawyers (solicitors) whose fees are based on the amount of financial settlement they make for their clients. They are best known for their work in lawsuits over car accidents, work-related injuries, etc.

29 October

Dear Brad

I'm sure I've met this editor of yours before. I used to know a
tall skinny journalist bloke who told just the sort of jokes you
describe. To cap it all, the magazine he edited over here had a
very similar readership to *Today's Christian World*. In fact, if it is
the same bloke, it will be *exactly* the same readership. Ask him
if he remembers George Smith, the poet whose work was too
bad even to be included in the Bad Poetry section of *Christian
Familiarity*, or whatever his rag was called. I'm sorry to hear he
liked my bit about Anglicanism – I thought it was quite good.

Christian radio, eh? Forgive us if we don't rush to accept
the material that you Christians in America would be quite
happy to send over. I suspect that you are motivated solely by
a desire to get rid of it. We have quite enough problems of
our own in that area, thank you very much. Sadly, Bradley, the
opportunities for quality Christian broadcasting in this
country have been sabotaged and seriously set back by
people who, having been put in charge of something like a
Sunday morning music programme, seem incapable of
speaking in anything but that strange, abstract, Christianese
drivel that never actually says anything. It goes something
like this:

'Good morning in the name of He who is most high. Through
His grace we are empowered to greet all our listeners, and a
special Spirit-directed arm of fellowship to all those who
have now yet put themselves under the mighty cleansing
blood of the covenant. For every unsaved boy, unredeemed

girl, sin-fettered brother, grace-resisting sister, and hell-bound aged one, here is young Cilla Black[1] singing "You're My World". And friends, harmless fun though it is to tap our feet and hum along with the tune, let's, at the same time as we enjoy being gay, ask ourselves whose world it really is, shall we? May God bless this song to you as you listen . . .'

It probably wasn't as bad as that, but it wasn't much better.

For the last thirty or so years the modern Church has sat itself down in public places and proceeded, with solemn and generally rather repellent insensitivity, to show the world how good it is at shooting itself in the foot. Writing, painting, dance, real music, beauty in the natural world, the reality of human relationships – these are all things that have been regarded with deep suspicion by whole sections of the Church, and particularly on those occasions when they suddenly find they have access to public platforms such as radio and television. Complexity and creativity are sucked out of the message before it's presented, leaving something so thin and pale, and yet so dogmatically assertive, that those who are exhorted to let it revolutionize their lives end up more annoyed than anything else. What a pathetic outcome. There are, thank God, some wonderful exceptions to this dismal style of outreach, but they're few and far between, and a lot of damage has already been done. The worst of this damage has been a strongly negative and almost disgusted response in many sections of the secular media to anything that's self-consciously, overtly 'Christian'. Personally, I think we'd be better off with Christians working in and with the media rather than trying to take it over.

Bradley, the bottom line is this. When the message is not granular – it grates.

Here's a poem (?) I wrote a few years ago when I was in one of those churches where Christians are supposed to be constructed out of large, easily handled, replaced and repaired parts. I wouldn't have shown it to them because it

would have provoked some very unpleasant and quite
unnecessary ministry.

Autumn is a fierce reply
To those who still deny your brooding heart
Flaming death in fading sun
The yearly mulching of elation, sadness, pain
A branch unclothed
The tatters flying, tentatively lying
Far more beautiful for dying
Rainbowed floating rain
The final breath
Softly whispering 'enough'
As memories come down like leaves
On old uneven pathways
Such a sweetness
See my breathing stands upon the air
And you, my oldest friend, are there
As evening falls
We pass between the tall park gates
A short cut to the town
A shiver moves the children's swings
The earth is soft and dark and rich
A Christmas cake
We know the grass
Will not be cut again this year
So down the tiled streets
The peopled rivulets
Perhaps towards some tea
In places that were ours but now have changed
Though early autumn darkness
Stares in, hungrily, through plate-glass windows still
Velveted by bright electric embers
We are glad to be there pouring tea
And pleased that we are laughing once again

Relieved that we are us once more

I have been troubled by a fear
That everything is gone
The fingertips of friendship cold and numb
But autumn is a season that returns
With intimations of the death of pain
And so, my friend, shall we
Spirit, you have brooded well
Melancholy autumn beauty
And the spring to come.

Ask Andy if he'd like to publish it in the TCW's 'Funny Old World' column.

George

P.S. I enclose a sketch of Cherry done by a friend of mine. It's a good likeness. Don't worry – a photograph of Diane without her sweater will be fine.

P.P.S. Thanks for forgiving me.

Note:
' Popular British singing star in the sixties.

November 4th

Dear George

Thank you for the rendering of Cherry. She's lovely.

Enclosed please find Diane's sweater (read: jumper). We had a drive at our church to give to the poor – giving clothes, dry goods, etc. – and Diane showed up with a bundle of her belongings, including the sweater. I gave an appropriate amount of money to the charity and immediately boxed it up for you. I hope it arrives intact. Maybe in a few years (if you haven't drooled all over it), if it isn't too much out of fashion, Cherry can wear it. In the meantime, *you* can.

My Andy is American – his last name is *Baker*. He's seen a couple of your letters so if he knows you, he hasn't admitted it.

That was a great poem, by the way.

I'll send a proper letter shortly.

Brad

17 November

Dear Bradley

You really are a size 12 medicinal cushion sometimes.
Thanks so much for your gift to this poverty-stricken cross-
dresser. When I saw the parcel I thought it was going to be
something exciting. Why couldn't you have boxed up the
money you gave instead? Or Diane herself? The jumper isn't
quite the same without her in it.

My Andy seemed to be English, but no intelligent
American would divulge his nationality in this country if he
wasn't forced to, would he? Ask one, and he'll tell you.

Hear from you soon,

George

P.S. How's your mother?

November 21st

Dear George

I think we've found one common denominator between our countries: Christianity in the Arts. Your description is a good one for the way things are here. There are a valiant few, of course, who want to bring honest and credible art to the Christian community (and society at large), but those people are generally regarded as impractical visionaries or flakes, or dismissed with that all-encompassing phrase: *non-commercial.*

It's terrible to generalize like that. Many Christians truly want to impact the Arts for Christ. But we've been removed from what the Arts are for so long that we don't know how to do it properly anymore. Paint a painting? Write a song? Perform a play? Only if there are tangible results with people rushing to accept Jesus thanks to whatever the effort was. Otherwise, why bother? (At least, that's the thinking of many Christian leaders who look at the Arts as simply a means to an end – or a substitute for their sermons. Very utilitarian.)

We're also a market-driven society, so the Arts will only get the attention of Christian publishers, etc. if they perceive a demand.

An example: I just got a flyer[1] for one of our local Christian bookstores. If we ever do get a book out of these letters and we can persuade a publisher to publish them, they'll *have to* bring you over just to see what an American Christian bookstore looks like. You have to see it to believe it. It's not limited to books, because Christian bookstores now carry a full line of *everything* that's available to the Christian home.

Rumor has it that this year someone's introducing a new line of designer Christian sportswear. And Step for the Savior Shoes. And Firm Believer Underwear. You think I'm kidding? Just walk the aisles and you'll see it all.

There will be kids' products galore. This year's favorite: the cute little character with the effeminate voice that looks like a kitchen utensil. He's called Saltshaker and sings a cute little song:

Shake a little here . . .
Shake a little there . . .
The salt of the earth should be everywhere!

Then there's the plethora of family 'help' books. Dr Jameson's latest is a 'best of' collection of his writings. It's called *What Strong-Willed Children Wish Their Parents Knew About Parental Love*. You still think I'm kidding, don't you?

And the *Bibles*! There's every version imaginable: KJV, NIV, NASB, NEB, NKJV, HMV, BVD, UB40 (just threw those in to make sure you were paying attention). Translated, Paraphrased, Amplified, Condensed, Revised, Reformed, Altered, Rejected, Processed, Poached and Over-Easy; in every form imaginable: hardback, softback, paperback, leatherback, mink, large-print, family-size, thin-line, pocket-size, wallet-size, and waterproof. And every category, too: Study Bibles, Topical Bibles, Illustrated Bibles (with graphs and line-drawings), Daily Devotional Bibles, Classical Bibles, Neo-Classical Bibles, Abstract Bibles, Chronological Bibles, Eschatological Bibles, Orthodoxical Bibles, De-Toxological Bibles (for recovering alcoholics), 'No Time To Read The Bible' Bibles (for people on the go: a 'greatest hits' approach with only one verse printed from each book), Precious Moments Bibles, Feminist Bibles, Alternate Lifestyle Bibles (no first chapter of Romans) and 'Back To The Bible' Bibles with just the original text (but they were out of print). I even saw one that had a reading lamp attached for use in bed. Do you still think I'm kidding?

There's one multi-million dollar ministry built around Refrigerator Magnets. Do you have refrigerator magnets in England? These have little Bible verses on them – with lovely little animals and characters, too.

And I haven't even mentioned the lucrative calendar industry.

I have mixed feelings about the whole thing. I realize that the booksellers are only a reflection of the demand from Christian buyers here. We want our homes filled with products that are easily identified as being of the Lord. Why not? It's no worse than Christian donut shops or insurance companies or, say, the Mechanics of the Master Garage I took my car to the other day. What makes it Christian? I'm not sure. I think the mechanics actually pray over the cars, or have their tools anointed.

It's all a matter of supply and demand.

You get my point? The Arts in the Christian Community will rise or fall based on the value that *mainstream* Christians attach to them – and publishers and record companies who'll take chances. Otherwise, our art had better be attached to a magnet.

Brad

P.S. I asked Andy about the 'Funny Old World' column you mentioned – since we don't have one in *Today's Christian World*. He asked if it was some kind of advice column. Do you have those there?

P.P.S. Just what did you mean by 'no intelligent American would divulge his nationality in this country if he wasn't forced to'? Look, bub, you guys would be speaking German if we hadn't bailed you out of *not one but two* world wars.

P.P.P.S. My mother is fine in spirit, but her health is deteriorating. The doctor won't give me a straight answer on what's happening to her.

Notes
' Flyer = leaflet.

26 November

Dear Bradley

Some questions: What is a 'flake'? We have them for breakfast.

Why do you insist on risking your future health by referring to me as 'bub'?

Are you really not aware that we allowed you to take part in our two wars in the same way that a caring parent would allow his awkward, inadequate child to take on some big grown-up task as a confidence-builder? I know it didn't work, but that's not our fault.

I have to admit that I found your comment about Bibles and refrigerator magnets very funny. We do have similar bookstores over here, as you know, but I don't think we've achieved the sheer variety of garbage that you describe.

I quite often go to Christian booksellers' conventions and the thing that always strikes me about them is the number of small, obscure organizations that are represented. You come across tiny, sentry-box type booths inhabited by one nervous but fanatically devout person in a threadbare suit, who describes himself as 'Universal Power Ministries'. He's usually giving out literature that's been typed on something so ancient and inkless that the result is a rather Braille-like indentation of the paper. I seem to detect a shadow of fear in the eyes of such folk. It is as if their presence at the event, and consequent exposure to the response of other Christians and the real world, has turned them into very wary little mammals indeed. They will only be really happy when they burrow back into the dimly lit back room with the heap of box-files, the neatly piled, light-bleached tracts and the god with the short back and sides who sits approvingly in the corner, looking oddly like the now-departed, plodding parent who used to call out three times a day that it was time for elevenses[1] – lunch – supper.

In answer to your question, 'Funny Old World' columns have nothing to do with advice. They contain bizarre, fascinating or amusing stories about something called 'real life'. We do have advice columns in some of our Christian magazines, though – some better than others. The following style has been around for a while, but I suspect that it passed its sell-by date some time ago. I've invented an 'adviser' called Alec Homecoil – just for you, Bradley.

Dear Alec Homecoil,

I see your photograph at the top of this column in every issue of the magazine. In your face I seem to see wisdom, compassion, spirituality, warmth, honesty, generosity and humility. Why is it, then, that, each month, I find myself wanting to punch you in the mouth as hard as I can?

Puzzled of Liphook

Dear Puzzled,

I'm so glad you asked me this question, because interestingly enough, I have experienced exactly the same problem myself. Often, when I am shaving in the morning, I look into the bathroom mirror and feel a profound desire to punch my own reflection in the mouth. I do resist the temptation for the following reasons:

(1) As good stewards we are called upon to guard our possessions, and mirrors can be quite expensive.

(2) The treatment of cut knuckles would add an unnecessary burden to an already over-stretched Health Service.

(3) Genuine Christians have no need to succumb to such negative impulses.

(4) Seven years' bad luck.
Yours sincerely,
  Alec Homecoil

P.S. I note with interest that you are resident in Liphook, a town where I once conducted a mission. Do give my love to all the super folks I met during that time of great blessing in 1923.

Dear Alec Homecoil,
   What should I do? My parents have fallen over a cliff, my business has gone bust, I have contracted a very serious illness, my house burned down a week ago, I have gone completely bald in less than a fortnight, I was mugged yesterday by a man who was better off than me, there are boils all over my face, my parrot is dead, my car's been stolen, my best friend's run off with my wife, I can't sleep, I can't find a job, my dentist says all my teeth have to come out, and I owe £50,000. I seem to be losing my joy.
   Battered of Grimsby

Dear Battered,
   I know that a Christian brother will forgive me if I indulge in a little gentle humour at his expense. It struck me, you see, as being terribly whimiscal that one who hails from Grimsby – renowned, of course, as a fishing port – should describe himself as being 'battered'[2]. I shall, with your permission, pass that one on to the little study group that I lead. It is good for Christians to have fun, and the members of my group have been unaccountably subject to a spirit of gloom for some time.
   As to your difficulties – well, I am so glad that you raised this issue because, oddly enough, I have experienced exactly the same problem myself. Some years ago I suffered three quite serious blows in the course of a single day:

   (1) I mislaid a roll of sellotape[3] that was by no means exhausted.

(2) A slight blemish appeared on my left arm and remained for some hours.

(3) I hope I am not an ungenerous person, but I was deeply hurt by the fact that a house guest, sadly taking advantage of my absence, over-indulged himself from a bottle of whisky that had been in the family for many years.

Naturally, in this very dark time, I was forced to ask myself some very hard questions about the reality of God and my own faith. Imagine my joy when, on that same day, the sellotape was found, the blemish disappeared and my guest brought me a brand new bottle of whisky which I have to this day. Not only that, but an anonymous gift of £50,000 was placed through my letter-box. I have never spent that money, and with interest it has now doubled. Dear friend – I want to say how struck I was by the final problem that you shared. I was given £50,000 and you desperately need exactly the same amount. What a coincidence. Bet you wish you were me! Yours sincerely,

Alec Homecoil

P.S. I have very strong recollections of leading a mission in Grimsby in 1937. Very few people came and, as far as I know, there were no conversions. The whole event was a tremendous success.

Dear Alec Homecoil,

I need your advice. Since I saw the light, I have been trying to convert my friend, but I don't seem to be getting anywhere, even though I talk about what I believe without stopping every single time we meet. Yesterday, when I went to her house, she refused to let me in and threw things at me from a top-floor window. Then she started screaming abuse and saying that if I ever went round again she'd drop something very heavy on me and shoot herself in the head, so that she'd go to hell and be sure of never seeing me again.

Persistent of Pudsey

Dear Persistent,

I think your friend is very close, don't you? How often it is that lost ones put up a show of token resistance just before their final submission. I think that, in a very real sense, your friend is actually saying, 'Thank you, dear persistent Christian chum, for not giving up. Come to my house again – soon!'

I must add that I am very glad that you raised this issue, because, singularly enough, I have experienced exactly the same problem myself. Some years ago, or possibly even before that, I headed up an evangelistic team involved in outreach to inner cities. When the time came for evaluation of the project we discovered that no one had made a commitment and twelve of the mission team had lost their faith. At the time this did seem just a little disappointing, but, marvellously, twenty-five years later, I met a man whose feelings about God were not entirely negative as a direct result of what he had heard at one of our mission evenings. A lesson in faith, I think.

Yours sincerely,

Alec Homecoil

P.S. Do say hello to Cyril and Doreen Grantley if you run into them – a dear old couple in their eighties, but full of life when I conducted a retreat in Pudsey in 1917.

Dear Alec Homecoil,

I believe that you are intending to hold seminars in this area quite soon under the title 'Generosity – A Gift from God'. Could you kindly tell me how much attendance at the seminars will cost?

Cleaned-out of Staines

Dear Cleaned-out,

The seminars you mention will cost £15 each, unless you are unemployed, a student or a pensioner, in which case, of course, you won't be able to come.

Yours sincerely,

 Alec Homecoil

P.S. There is an entry in my diary for June 1936 which reads, 'Saw several come through at Staines', but I am not sure if this refers to success in a mission or relief from a particularly uncomfortable medical condition.

Dear Alec Homecoil,

 I have experienced problems with doubt all my life, but I have somehow managed to persuade myself and quite a lot of other people that I can still be a Christian if I don't believe in the virgin birth, the resurrection, divine healing or any kind of hell. Now, though, as I approach the end of my life, I begin to feel a little nervous.

 Retired of Durham

Dear Retired,

 I am so glad that you raised this issue, because, fascinatingly enough, I have experienced exactly the same problem myself. I solved it by talking things over with my local Anglican clergyman. Why don't you do the same?

Yours sincerely,

 Alec Homecoil

P.S. You're not . . . ? No, never mind, it doesn't matter.[4]

If you have any pressing problems, Bradley, just pass them on to me and I'll get Alec to sort them all out for you. Speaking of which – keep me posted about your mother. I've actually been praying for her. God must have said, 'George who? Oh, that George! Good heavens, haven't heard from him in years . . . '

George

Notes

¹ Elevenses is a late morning snack.

² In Britain, batter is used in the preparation of traditional fish and chips; fish are coated in batter before frying.

³ Sellotape is British for Scotch™ tape.

⁴ Alec's question implies that he believes the writer to be the infamous former Bishop of Durham (in Britain), the Rt Revd David Jenkins, best known for his sermons, books and articles calling into question many of the basics of Christian faith.

December 1st

Dear George

Thanks for your letter.

To briefly answer your questions: (1) a 'flake' is a space-cadet; (2) no comment on 'bub'; (3) the depth of your delusion about our participation in World Wars One and Two is obviously the result of your having lost an entire empire only to become a large aircraft carrier for us. Enough said about that.

Thank you for the Alec Homecoil letters. They were *very* funny and reminiscent in this country of many of our Christian radio talk show hosts. I get the impression that Alec has (or thinks he has) *personally* experienced everything there is to experience in life. I'd love to hear what he has to say about menopause. When did he experience it and what did he learn?

You asked about my mom. Well, I went to see her yesterday. It's a weekly routine now. She had to leave her job at the bank because of her health (and because she's *well past* retirement age – but she refused to consider retirement before this) so now she has a lot of time on her hands.

Our first exercise when I arrive is to read her any letters I have from you. I'm not sure I'm getting your accent right, but I try. Do you remember Dick Van Dyke's accent in *Mary Poppins*? It's something like that. I think you'd be impressed.

She's very interested in our thoughts about being a Christian (in *either* country). I think you'd like my mother, George. Not everyone does. She can be a bit prickly at times – and seems to be getting more so. For example, last week she blasted her pastor for a sermon he preached about the role of women in the Church. 'The Bible says what it says. Why can't you folks leave it alone?' she asked. The pastor answered that the issue was 'a little more complex than that'. My mother locked her eyes on his and said, 'Physics is complex. A congressional Bill is complex. My son's dating life is complex. The role of women in the Church is not complex.'

I asked her about this confrontation and she suggested that we make such issues complex because it's the only way this generation can prove how enlightened it is. 'How else can we prove all the previous generations of Christians wrong? You went to Bible college, did you read the writings of Augustine, Pascal, Wesley, Whitefield or Talmadge?' I said that she knew full well that I didn't. 'Of course you didn't. Why should you? They're only writings from some of the greatest Christian minds we've ever had.' Now do you see where I get my flippancy?

She went on, 'How else are you going to understand Christianity today if you don't understand where it came from? Did you think all we believe as Christians suddenly popped into somebody's head during a youth pizza night?'

I explained defensively and impatiently (as I often do with my mother) that Christianity is different now than it was when those writers wrote – or when she was younger. We're faced with different problems and all that.

'Christianity hasn't changed. It's the Christians who have changed,' she complained.

'How?' I asked.

'High expectations. You expect too much,' she said. I rolled my eyes. I knew I had touched on one of her pet peeves and wouldn't escape for at least another hour. 'You kids expect that there are certain rights we're entitled to exercise. Everyone wants their rights, but nobody wants to sacrifice anything. You expect to be committed to principle only as long as it's convenient.'

I waited the storm out, certain she'd tell me for the trillionth time how, when she was young, she walked in her bare feet to school in ten inches of snow. 'You believe you should get whatever you want whenever you want it. That's what's wrong with our culture ("our culture" meaning we Americans, George). Somewhere along the line we decided we're God's chosen people and he's answerable to us. I've looked in the Bible, I can't find it. It was different when I was younger. We had more patience. We knew how to wait – for answers, for God, for other people to finish using the bathroom, for the natural conclusions to our lives. Nowadays, everybody wants everything right away.'

'So, we're too impatient now? Is that what you're saying? Look, I remember the time that Dad – '

'That's *not* what I'm saying. That's not the problem. It's one of the problems. Another problem is that you like to summarize your problems. Pigeon-hole them. Put them where you can find them. And then you pigeon-hole the answers too. You put the problem here and put the answer there and think you have solved it. Where's the faith in that?'

'Where are you getting this stuff?' I asked her, annoyed on behalf of my generation of Christians. 'What books have you been reading lately? Are you trying to tell me that you think Christians today don't have enough faith? I don't remember *your* generation being filled with giants of faith.'

'I didn't say you don't have enough faith. And don't get snippy. I'm still your mother, even if I am dying. All I'm saying is that *we* – does that make you feel better? – *we* don't allow faith proper time to nurture and grow. We read all the quick-step books and use all the catchphrases – they look nice on the page, but they have little to do with what we're experiencing.' She coughed violently for a moment, then continued. 'Here's something I read the other day: "Christians are works in progress, with faith so fragile it withers under the harsh breath of daily struggle, yet so enduring it blossoms under a concrete crisis." But how do you know unless your faith comes up against it? You can't tell how strong you are until your weaknesses are tested. I never knew how real God was to me until I came down with cancer . . .'

With that, she went into another violent coughing spell and I knew we had talked too much. I told her to rest and left.

I thought about it later. Of course she's right. I just hate to admit it when she launches into another one of her sermons (a conditioned response after a lifetime). We Americans are so consumer-based. We really are used to getting what we want whenever we want it. You name it, you can get it fast. We don't like to wait in long bank lines, so they created ATMs[1] and drive-in banking. You want something to eat in the middle of the night? 24-hour restaurants and grocery stores. Wanna buy something? Just call this toll-free number,[2] operators are standing by, any time, day or night. Do you have physical pain? Take a drug and relief comes fast, fast, fast. It's an instant-gratification society. Is that how it works in England?

Mom's right. It really *has* affected how we perceive Christianity. It's as if we now believe we can take a pill called 'Instant Christian' and automatically arrive in the Lord. No process, no pain. Just a little 'Instant Christian' and those prayers will be answered when we want them answered – those nagging verses from the Bible will become clear as glass – those troublesome personality quirks will simply disappear. Is sin a problem? Not for 'Instant Christian'! A quick application and they're gone in record time. What about conflicts with other Christians? Don't worry. 'Instant Christian' will eliminate them before you can say 'thorn in the flesh'. And we don't have to worry about those unsightly gray areas, either. Just use 'Instant Christian' and everything will turn to black and white. It's fast, easy – and we won't have to think about it. We can use 'Instant Christian' anywhere: at home, at church, in your Bible studies – even on your boat on

Sunday morning! It's simple to apply and requires no additional application. 'Instant Christian' – because, in this modern world, who has the time to wait for change? Just get your Visa or MasterCard handy and call toll-free! Operators are standing by.

Sorry, I got carried away. But that's the way it seems Christians think over here. At least, I know I do. How about there?

Tag. You're it.

Brad

P.S. I don't mean to make my mom sound like a crotchety old woman – but she really is. See, she had three children in her prime and then her husband died. Several years later she remarried and – surprise!! – I showed up after her biological clock had promised otherwise.

P.P.S. Before she fell asleep, Mom told me to tell you hello.

Notes
[1] ATM = automatic teller machines = cash-point machines.

[2] Toll-free numbers = freephone numbers.

7 December

Dear Brad

First, if I ever visit you over there I shall expect a bowl of space cadets for breakfast every day. Will they keep still while I pour milk all over them? What *are* you talking about???

Secondly, I can't just let your statement about this country being a 'large aircraft carrier for America' pass by without comment. It's a very large aircraft carrier, Bradley, and you know it. You're right about the empire, though. We've given more countries back to themselves than you've had Big Macs.

Bradley, I think your mother sounds quite wonderful. She also sounds a bit like me, if that isn't too insulting. I'd like to get her alone in my study and ask her what she thinks about everything under the sun. Tell her that if she comes I'll buy a bag of logs specially in her honour and light a fire in the grate. She can sit beside it in the corner on the beaten-up armchair with the rust-coloured covers that Gemma used to use when I was working at home and we took breaks to eat together. I'll put one of the side lamps on and light a couple of fat candles so that there will be plenty of moving shadows. It'll feel so cosy and warm. I'll sit on my swivel chair and revolve in an intellectual sort of way, thinking of clever things to say that will impress her or make her argue with me. Cherry can bring us cake and coffee – or tea or hot chocolate, or whatever your mother likes best – and we'll tell each other how ridiculous this stupid rumour about dying is, because we're going to be alive and chatting and feeling warm together for ever and ever and ever . . .

I agree with what your mother says about materialism. It might not be quite as bad in this country, but, as far as the Church is concerned, it seems to have crept into those very areas where people might say they were above such crassness. And it really is very subtle. I can express it best by rewriting a very famous piece of scripture for you:

For God so loved the world that he gave his only Son, that whosoever believes in him, keeps his nose clean and makes a significant but sensibly balanced contribution to church life in terms of time and cash, shall have a reasonable expectation of material comfort, physical good health, and ongoing prosperity in the fields of business and emotional relationships, with guidance provided as and when necessary so that opportunities in all these areas shall not be missed or wasted. Oh, yes, I nearly forgot – he won't perish, and eternal life gets thrown in as well.

Eternal life doesn't seem to count for much these days, does it?

I read an article the other day by a Christian fellow who was describing his darkest hour – the time when his faith was most challenged. The trouble was that, like old Alec Homecoil, his darkest hour wasn't anything like the kind of darkest hour that Jesus warned his followers about. This bloke was an artist and he'd put some pictures into an exhibition, obviously with high hopes of selling a good number of them. He didn't sell as many as he'd hoped and he was devastated. What was God playing at? Then a radio arts programme of some kind fell through just before he was due to become involved. God had screwed up again. He said that these two disappointments severely tested his faith. But he didn't say anything about the quality or lack of quality in his pictures, nor did he mention any of the reasons – possibly very good reasons – why the radio thing didn't come off. I don't mean I don't understand disappointment. It's never easy to take failure. I just mean that we seem to have come an awful long way from Paul announcing that he'd experienced shipwreck, flogging, depression, hunger and stoning, and then asking who'd like to make a commitment.

I have to go and cook tea now, and get Cherry ready for her Arctic Survival class. I'll write some more a bit later.

It's eight o'clock in the evening, Brad. Cherry's skis, snow-suit and oxygen mask are tucked tidily away in the wardrobe and I finished putting her to bed some time ago. We prayed for your mum after the story tonight. When we'd finished Cherry asked if she should send one of her pictures to cheer Mrs Miller up – what is your mother's first name, for goodness sake, Bradley? I said I was sure she'd love to have a picture. I'll put it in with this letter. Tell your mother that if she doesn't like it, she'll have to lie through her teeth. She won't mind – she's a good Christian.

I read the earlier part of this letter through just now. I feel very ashamed. Talk about A-levels[1] in hypocrisy. How could I talk about other people being discontented when I've more or less refused to even talk to God since Gemma died? You know how people sometimes say that the Lord's given them a verse, don't you? I've been finding that a real pass-the-sick-bag comment in recent years, probably because I was jealous. Well, I've got my come-uppance. Less than ten minutes ago I found a verse in Exodus that hit me like a bullet. It was God telling Pharaoh that he wanted Israel released so that they could worship him in the desert. I should have been doing that, Brad, but the hurt was too bad and it was easier to cuddle the pain. I said sorry a few moments ago – what do you think about that?

Do you want to know what God said in reply? He said, 'Well, yes, that's all very well for you. I suppose you expect me to just turn round and forgive you after the way you've treated me. I'm not one to complain, but frankly . . .'

You know what he's like.
It's good to be back.

George

P.S. The Christmas machine is really rolling here now.
Cherry's made a list. Tell your mum not to die before
Christmas. We're making something for her.

Notes
[1] A-levels are the exams which qualify British students for
university.

December 12th

Dear George

Usually I love Christmas, but this year it's slipping past
without the fanfare I usually like to give it. (I'm a sucker for all
the hustle and bustle, the music, the good fellowship . . .) It's
probably because of my mom. I'm spending a lot more time
with her. She has *that look* now, you know what I mean? The
look cancer victims get when they're hovering between yes
and no, between remission and resignation. Pale, hollow-
eyed, thin. But she still has the spark of life and seems
determined not to give up before God tells her to.

I decorated her house this past weekend. She wasn't very
interested. She kept saying she would rather be with *you* in
England, arguing, next to that fire you described. I felt a
twinge of jealousy. She doesn't get that bright-eyed when I
turn on the space heater[1] and offer to read her some of my
articles for *Today's Christian World*.

She's pleased that you're on speaking terms with God
again. So am I. But take it from someone who feels like he's
actually *in* the desert: it's no picnic and there isn't a lot of
worshipping going on.

I'm thinking of changing churches. I have this itch . . . a
craving to get away from the standard Evangelical church
menu of Christmas choruses and pageants, and ninety-
minute sermons about the *real* meaning of Christmas, and a
tradition that goes back only as far as last year's marketing
survey from Willow Creek.[2] I want something *truly* traditional.
Something that speaks the words that my heart can't conjure
up right now. I want *liturgy* and *form* and *worship* in a big church

where you actually kneel when you pray and you go to an altar to take communion and . . . I must be out of my mind. Mom will accuse me of going Catholic or something.

But if I change churches, I may have to give up Christians Anonymous. No great loss, I suppose. Diane resists any attempt by me to get closer than being 'just friends at a Bible study.' I'm trying not to take it personally. My guess, though, is that she wants a spiritual giant – not *moi* (who can't even muster the faith to speak in tongues). Oh well . . .

After our normal study (we're lost in Romans somewhere), Dave asked the group if we've made any progress with 'who we are as Christians'. There was a threatening tone in his voice – as if we were in *big* trouble if we hadn't figured it out after all this time. Carl explained that he once knew some people who were confused about their Christianity but after he explained it to them clearly in an exegetical manner that took into consideration the contextual meaning of the original Greek while allowing for the nuances of translation, interpretation and personal application, then the importance of the redemptive work of the cross has a transcendent quality beyond the cultural historicity of the event.

I hastily made a list of some of those words to look up in my concordance when I got home.

Karen enthusiastically raised her hand and said she wanted to share something she had written in her journal on the subject. Dave nodded for her to do so and she did. It was everything I would have expected from a woman with a 'Precious Moments' mentality. I could barely contain myself and decided to scribble down every cliché I heard (they were sprinkled throughout):

'I've found in my walk with the Lord that my quiet times help defeat any struggle with confusion I might have as a believer . . . Remember: Satan is the author of confusion, but God owns the bookstore . . . If God says it and I believe it, then that's good enough for me . . . Get back to the Bible . . . focus on the family . . . have insight for living . . . Christianity isn't a religion, it's a way of life . . . Just let go and let God . . . God hates the sin, but loves the sinner . . . He's the real thing . . . Trust and obey . . . Give the Master charge . . .

Oh, Lord, glorify thy name.'[3]

It was endless. All she left out was to put your hand in the hand of the One who stilled the water, and to honk if you love Jesus because God's will for your life is to have it and have it more abundantly, if you'll only claim it in the power of his name with a servant's spirit. Have a nice forever. What a blessing!

Ruth saw what I was doing and kept nudging me to behave.

How is it possible? How can Karen really have such a mind-numbingly simple idea of Christianity? (But she does, George. She *really* does.) Then I figured it out. I saw her Christmas shopping in town the other day. As I watched her walk with her armload of expensively wrapped gifts to her BMW, where her well-to-do husband waited while talking on his car phone to some client somewhere, I realized that it's *easy* for her. Her life is full of the kind of constants that reaffirm the simplest acts of faith: a home, a dutiful and reasonably wealthy husband, a God who didn't demand too much of her. Yes, the answer was *very* easy.

I felt a twinge of shame for thinking such things, George, but I didn't repent. I couldn't. Christianity is plenty easy for people who lead a perfect life.

This is disgustingly morose. Sorry. A Christmas card is on its way, along with a little something for Cherry. Merry Christmas, George, and as Tiny Tim would say . . . 'Tag. You're it.'

Brad

P.S. Oh – sorry. My mother's name is Mary.

Notes

¹Space heater = a portable heater.

²Willow Creek Church (in Illinois) has been a trend-setter and model for many American churches in its forms of worship services, outreaches, etc.

³The British equivalent would be translated as follows:

'I've found in my walk with the Lord that my quiet times help defeat any struggle with confusion I might have as a believer. Remember: Satan is the author of confusion, but God owns the bookshop. And if God says it and I believe it, then that's good enough for me. Tonight I was given a word of knowledge. That word was *renewal*.

We need to ally our evangelicals, care for the family, and spring to the harvest. We're all the King's kids who must remember that Christianity isn't a religion, it's a way of life. Simply let go and let God, for he hates sin, but loves the sinner. He's for us.

Trust and obey.

We must tell the nations about the King's way by giving shouts of joy on our march for Jesus. With meekness and majesty, we have to let shine Jesus shine while we live under the shadow of his wing in this present darkness.

Oh, Lord, glorify thy name.'

18 December

Dear Brad

Sit down in some quiet place before you read any more of this letter. I'm not going to write another word until you do. No. Bradley, it's no use reading on until you've done what you're told. Sit down! Are you settled now? Are you comfortable? Good. Let me reach across the metaphorical ocean and take your metaphorical hand so that I can gently break some news that will leave you hurt and bewildered and disoriented. I wish I didn't have to do this, but genuine friends don't flinch from passing on hard truths. Have a tissue ready. Here it is, Brad:

THERE IS NO SEARS DEPARTMENT STORE IN THIS COUNTRY.

The Sears token[1] you sent for Cherry was very generous, but there's nowhere to exchange it. I know you Yanks fondly believe that the rest of the world is merely a pale replica of the good old USA, but it's not true. Just as we have no Sears department store, so we have no White House, no Super Bowl, no Broadway, no Cadillacs, no Mafia, no hillbillies, no good-looking politicians, no Hollywood, no Disneyland, nor any of the other things that have made your country grate for so many years.

I'll get a Boots token for the same amount and send the other one back to you. Say thanks to Mary for me. I'll let you know later on what Cherry gets with it. Boots is a place where you can get anything from contraceptives to corn-plasters,[2] depending on what sort of evening you're planning. I suspect that my daughter, who is six-going-on-twenty-five, will probably opt for one of those awful *Baywatch*-type dolls that you can dress and undress to your heart's content.

How much do you think a real one would cost? Now that I'm a bit more straightened out about Gemma and me and God, I have to admit that I've started to notice women a lot more than I had been. Nothing unseemly you understand, just plain unbridled lust – that sort of thing. Seriously, I have begun to realize how lonely I am. There's no hurry, and I'm happy to let the divine dating agency look after the details, but, well – it would be nice.

Sex has been a problem area in the Church over here for some time. Such a powerful force to control, especially when you really are trying to be the sort of person that God wants you to be. Christian literature on the subject tends (with a few notable exceptions) to be rather insipid, while secular reading matter varies from easily available pornography, through genuinely helpful stuff, to articles in women's magazines telling readers how they can knit their own orgasms. I don't know how we manage to produce any baby Christians at all. Ask your mother what she thinks – bet she knows more about the subject than you ever guessed.

Bradley, you tell your mum that we think about her every single day. Cherry and I have written a letter to God and put it in an envelope so that we can hold it up to him every day and ask him to do what we've asked. This is what it says:

Dear God,
We want Bradley and his mummy to have the best, best time they possibly can for this Christmas and for always. We don't know what's going to happen and we don't want to tell you what to do, but we know you love them very much, and it's nearly time for presents. Tell Father Christmas to bring some good, big things for both of them. Make sure they're safe and don't go in Central Park at night.
Love from Cherry and George

Mostly Cherry's words, but my agreement. I like the bit about Central Park. Don't you go in there at night, Mary.

You're right to feel morose at the moment, Brad. Feel what you feel. It's okay. Have a Christmas.

Love from George and Cherry

Notes:

[1]Token = gift certificate.

[2]Corn-plasters = Band-Aids for foot problems.

27th December

Dear George

Thank you for the letter and the terrific angel to put on the top of Mom's tree. It arrived Christmas Eve. Mom was deeply touched, though when I wanted to just stick the thing on the tree, she rebuked me and turned the placement of the angel into a formal-almost-religious experience, complete with the angel held high and a hymn being sung ('Angels We have Heard on High') as we marched to the tree and put it on top. When I teased Mom about 'going liturgical' she just shrugged.

I took that opportunity to tell her what I told you about leaving my church in order to find something 'more traditional'. I braced myself for an argument. Instead, she said she understood completely. Good thing, since I had already made plans to go to the Christmas Eve service at an old, old Episcopal church (built in 1927). I was surprised to realize that the Episcopalians are American Anglicans. What a coincidence, huh? I was even more surprised when she asked to go with me. The church is cathedral-like and very reverent, and the Christmas Eve service was one of the most beautiful I've ever seen. It scratched the itch, George. I'll have to go back. Mom agreed.

Christmas Day was spent quietly enough – just the two of us and the obligatory calls from my half-brother and two half-sisters. They're scattered around the country and have families of their own. I also get the impression that they're avoiding Mom's illness. True to the American spirit, we avoid dealing with death at every turn.

Sorry about the Sears gift certificate (token?). I really thought they were an international chain. Tell me how much the Boots certificate was and I'll send you a check right away. Otherwise, plan to use the Sears certificate when you come to visit (hint, hint).

I talked to Mom about your renewed interest in the opposite sex. She noted that your preoccupation with Diane's sweater telegraphed your interest, whether you realized it or not. She mentioned a seed in winter or something like that.

Somehow it doesn't seem appropriate to ramble on about sex right after Christmas, but I will say that American Christians take it very seriously. After years of not discussing it or drilling into adolescent minds how horrible it is if you abuse it, we now have a smorgasbord of books proclaiming it as God-ordained and pleasurable and wonderful (in the context of marriage, of course) and even how to do it in a true spiritual way. Don't ask, I don't know. As a Single Man, I can't relate and I find there are very few books for my situation (being single and staying pure, etc.) – at least none that I'm interested in reading. Illustrations would help.

Of course, being a single male at the age of twenty-eight is tantamount to proclaiming myself gay to all the world anyway. (A worthwhile discussion for our book, I think: What happens to singles in England? What do you think of homosexuality? – and don't blame me for asking because you brought up the whole sex subject.) I have an experience to tell you about, but not now.

Tell me one other thing: why the prayer about Central Park? It's a thousand miles away from me. But tell Cherry my mother and I both appreciated the letter to God. I'm not feeling morose now, simply resigned.

I got a nice little note from Diane, by the way. She is convinced that Mom is going to be healed – if we have enough faith. I wonder how much faith will be a suitable bribe for God?

Brad

P.S. Happy New Year!

4 January

Dear Bradley

I've been picturing the following scene: It's Christmas Eve in heaven. (I'm afraid they probably don't have a Sears department store in heaven either, Brad, but you'll just have to get by the best you can.) There's been some excitement in the Golden City lately because Bradley Miller of Colorado, America, has started to see a way forward for his faith. His route, carefully worked out by God and cleared of obstacles specially for him by an angelic road-gang, if he did but know it, runs through the traditional Church in general, and, in particular, an old, old Episcopal church (built in 1927) near his home.

God is *so* excited. He's had a very soft spot for this young American for many years, and now, at last, after a great deal of planning and organization, something of real spiritual significance is going to happen. On Christmas morning, the Father of all mankind is pacing the floor of heaven, awaiting angelic intelligence of Bradley Miller's response to the experience that has been designed to flood him with an awareness of the power and love of God in his life. At last the Miller angel, tired and haggard beyond his years, presents himself before his Master and kneels respectfully.

'Well?' demands God, 'don't just kneel there – tell me what he said! Did he speak in tongues at last? Did he break into hymns of praise? Did he dance in the Spirit? What did he say? Tell me!'

'He said – '

'Yes, what?'

'He said, "It scratched the itch."'

'I'm so glad he was pleased,' says God, slightly miffed. '

I'm glad you were pleased as well, Brad. As you must have gathered from what I wrote back in autumn, I tend to go in that sort of direction as well, but only because it's right for me. Everyone else can join the Ninth Day Amber-Bryanites for all I care. Goodness, how relieved everyone else must be.

I'm glad I didn't have to be there to watch your family taking obligatory steps. How dreary. You've never told *me* anything about your father. Dead? Alive? Goody? Baddy? Christian? Episcopalian?

We spent Christmas with my divorced sister, Jenny, and her three little girls, up in Bishop Aukland, near Durham. (If you come over next year I must show you Durham – such a beautiful city.) We had a wonderful time for three very good reasons.

One, it's the first Christmas since Gemma's death that I haven't been locked into the business of clenching my pain with both fists and pretending I was all right for Cherry's sake. I actually felt happy!

Two, I was back with God – nearly made a complete idiot of myself on Christmas morning at church. I just couldn't stop the tears when I went up for communion. The Body of Christ, broken for me; the Blood of Christ, shed for me – staggering. Good job it was one of the more stolid Anglican churches. They were more likely to offer me hay-fever tablets than ministry.

Third, it was good to be with Jenny and the girls. Cherry had a wonderful time being all girly with her cousins. It was worth hacking through forests of underwear in the bathroom every morning and evening to see her so happy. It's the first time Jenny and I have properly supported each other since Gemma died. Jenny's husband, who provides excellent opportunities for the exercise of forgiveness, left her eighteen months ago and she really has had to struggle. We got slightly tipsy together on Boxing Day[2] evening. I hope God didn't mind too much . . .

You asked me what happens to single people in England. Well, the short answer is that they tend to be marginalized by people from the church, not for malicious reasons, but just because people forget that, if you are on your own, you don't always have the confidence to inflict yourself on families. You need to be invited specifically to join people in their homes, rather than be told it's 'all right to drop in any time'. I feel awful when I think back to the way Gemma and I were with single people. We were so insensitive – but we didn't understand, you see? Besides all that, the Church as an institution is very much geared to family activity, and you can feel very uncared for at times. I've tended to sulk about this in the past, but I think I'm going to make more of an effort to let people know how singles feel – then it'll be up to them.

As for the issue of homosexuality – well, I am gay, as you've probably already guessed. I'm not really gay. Sorry, Bradley. I only said that so you could find out how your perception of me changed at the moment when you thought I *was* homosexual. Oh, Brad, I find this such a difficult subject. Can't I chicken out?

'No, you can't'

Who said that?

'Me.'

Oh, all right, then. If you drove me into a corner and threatened to play Scottish music to me until I came out with what I really thought, I'd have to say that I don't think homosexual behaviour is something that God is happy about, any more than he's happy about the way in which vast numbers of heterosexuals conduct themselves. But more importantly than any of that, I believe – I know – that it's no easier now to outguess God in individual situations than it was when Jesus was here in the flesh. I've been told to love people and not judge them. I'd rather do that than home in on their sexuality. O*h biscuits*! I *don't know*!

You had an experience? Oh, dear . . .

Ask Diane if she's willing to come and get her jumper if it

turns out she's wrong about your mum being healed. That'll test her faith, if not yours.

Love to Mary from Cherry and I. The fire's all ready to light if she wants to come.

Love from George

P.S. Central Park is regularly presented to British audiences through fact and fiction as the most dark and dangerous place in America.

Notes

[1] Miffed = annoyed.

[2] Boxing Day is the day after Christmas and celebrated in Britain as a holiday. Its name is derived from giving boxes of gifts to those in need.

January 16th

Dear George

You're a funny man. You should try writing comedy for a living. I think 'scratched an itch' is an appropriate thing to say. Jesus used commonplace analogies like that all the time. I can't imagine the woman at the well complaining that his 'living water, never thirst again' line was trite because it over-simplified the vastness of spiritual refreshment.

Speaking of writing, Andy wanted me to tell you that mail response to your first letter (printed in the January issue, which came out in December – go figure[1]) has been enormous. Everyone loves it. He now wants to print *only your* letters as a 'Letters from England' column because he thinks audiences will enjoy the perspective more.

I'm so happy for you.

My Dad is alive and used to be a music minister until he left my mother to make music with the church organist. I haven't seen or spoken to him in a couple of years. I'm not even sure he knows about Mom's condition, since I haven't called to tell him.

Look, if you can't decide what you think of homosexuality, then write what the general attitude among British Christians is. In America, it's a very divisive issue. What Christians here think about gays depends on whether you're Liberal or Conservative.

Since I was raised a Conservative, I confess that my immediate temptation when discussing homosexuality is to invoke the names of Sodom and Gomorrah, along with a host of Old Testament laws, Romans 1 . . . you know. But then I

111

remember an experience I had a few years ago during my brief tenure attending Bible college. The Bible college was an attempt to assuage the guilt I often felt about going forward to become a minister and never making good on it. So I went to the college and worked part-time at my church (then) as a youth minister. Those were pretty heady days – first-century Greek, eschatology, hermeneutics. Everyone was very proud of me, my mom especially. And I seemed to have the golden touch with the youth group, coming up with lots of things for the kids to do, counseling them, being their friend. I was 'wise before my years' everyone said.

One night I was studying at home (a rented room, actually). There was a gentle knock on the door. I barely heard it. I opened it to find Martin standing there – one of the young men from the church. He was in his teens and I remember liking him instinctively when I first met him. He was personable and outgoing without being too pushy. At all times, his behavior was very appropriate for a fine, upstanding Christian. A more well-balanced and stable young man I don't think I ever knew. I was surprised by his visit. 'Martin? What are you doing out at this hour?' I asked him.

'Walking. Thinking,' he replied. I invited him in and he reluctantly accepted. He kept asking if he was bothering me, if I was counseling someone. I assured him that I was only reading and asked what I could do for him. Martin asked, 'Is that how you start your counseling? With that question?' I shrugged, then asked if I was about to counsel *him*. He said he wasn't sure if I *could* counsel him – if anyone could.

I felt a little impatient. 'What's on your mind, Martin?' He was very jittery and paced in small steps. He replied that he had a problem, though it wasn't a recent problem. He wasn't sure he could talk about it because it was a secret. I asked him if the problem was with a secret or if he had a secret problem. 'Yes,' he answered. Then he said that, for as long as he could remember, he had this particular problem. It was a secret he kept to himself for years.

'I've had to keep it a secret. If anyone knew . . . if anyone even *guessed* . . . I don't know what I'd do.' From there, Martin played a cat-and-mouse game in our conversation – hinting at his problem, but not saying what it was. He was testing me, I knew, but I couldn't imagine why. However I must have done something to pass because he suddenly decided to share his secret. He said he was a homosexual.

I tried to be very calm. I didn't want to betray any sense of shock. I asked him why he thought he was a homosexual. 'I just am. I know it. I feel it,' he replied.

All my studies in first-century Greek and eschatology suddenly evaporated like steaming ink from a white page, leaving the page empty. I had nothing to call on. No quote. No insight. And the only scripture that came to mind was condemning. I tried to be rational. 'A lot of boys your age go through periods of confusion about their sexuality.'

Martin gave me a steely look, 'I'm not confused. I know what I am.'

'Then why are you here? Obviously you've made up your mind. What do you want from me?' I asked.

'Help. You have to help me,' he replied.

'I don't know if I can when your mind is already made up.' He didn't know what I meant by his mind being 'made up'. 'Well, if you're determined to *be* a homosexual . . .'

He frowned, 'I'm not determined to be one, I *am* one. I don't know how it happened. I . . . I just have . . . these desires. I always have. I've tried to make them go away. I've prayed again and again.' I reminded him of scripture, but he cut me off with a voice choked with emotion. 'I know, Brad. I've read the Bible. I'm a worm. I'm accursed. And I want to change. I want to. I *have* to. Pray with me. Please.'

So I prayed with him, for repentance, for healing, for guidance, for anything and everything we thought would help. We prayed until we were drained of anything left to pray for. Martin came back to me on a regular basis and, during the next few weeks, it became more and more difficult. The

113

deeper we delved into his 'secret', the less equipped I was to help him. I didn't have the training or the resources. It's not like they had classes at the Bible college about it.

Sometimes I had bouts of anger as I was *sure* he wasn't trying hard enough to change. Sometimes I shouted at him that the Lord would change him if he *truly* repented. Once Martin fell to his knees, weeping, 'Then I repent! A million times I repent! Change me, God! Create in me a clean heart, O Lord . . .'

We discussed it, debated it, searched the scriptures. He had moments when he thought he had changed – an occasional date with a girl he liked, but . . . only as a friend. And there were other times when we cried together because he had been weak. It became frustrating. I didn't know what to do.

One night he said simply that he had reached a fork in the road. I asked him what he meant. He confessed that he couldn't go on like this anymore. He couldn't be both a Christian and a homosexual. 'I'm at war with myself.'

'We all are – in some form or another,' I observed.

'But I hate it. I must be . . . *want to be* only one . . . at peace.'

'God will give you peace, Martin,' I said, but the words sounded trite.

'The same way he *healed* me? Some God.'

I snapped at him for being disrespectful to God and Martin said he'd leave. It was a waste of time – all these weeks. One failure after another. He was beyond help, he said. He knew it even before he came to me. I disagreed, but he wouldn't listen. He left so suddenly. I was sure I wouldn't see him again.

I felt he would abandon his faith and pursue this other life – to embrace the darkness of his secret. I would have gone after him to . . . To what? What did I have left to offer? I didn't know how to help. Only then did I decide I should've taken this whole problem to my pastor – someone older and *truly* wiser. Maybe I should've done that at the start.

I saw Martin again, one more time. I spoke at his funeral service. He couldn't live with *either* life – so he chose no life at all. Many were shocked. Many didn't understand how or why such a nice young man would take his own life. They didn't know. How could they? Martin was so good at keeping secrets.

So am I . . . now.

For a while, the folks at church continued to think of me as a good youth leader – 'wise beyond his years'. I knew better. So did Martin.

So I left Bible college and the job as youth leader and moved to the opposite end of the country to be a writer.

Does that answer your question?

Brad

Notes

¹ Go figure = fancy that!

31 January

Dear Brad

I found your letter very moving. I'm sure there are lots of
Martins around (with a whole variety of problems) and the
thought of them being hounded into this kind of dreadfully
negative resolution breaks my heart. I have a friend – let's call
him Dave – who sought counselling for an aspect of his
personality that was likely to get him into very serious
trouble if he ever gave way to his inclinations. Being a life –
long evangelical, Charismatic Christian, Dave applied for
help to a well-known Christian organization. He was
allocated a 'counsellor' who began the contact with bright
faith and optimism but became increasingly petulant and
aggressive as it became clear that my friend was not going to
prop up anyone's view of God by agreeing that he was healed
when he wasn't. In the end the counsellor, who was far too
young and should never have been given the job anyway, ran
out of ideas. He told Dave that if he hadn't 'changed' within a
week he would be deliberately placing himself outside the
will of God, and therefore likely to forfeit his salvation.

Dave was absolutely terrified by what this idiot – I mean
this well-meaning but deluded brother – said. Wouldn't you
be? Fortunately, he then discovered a long-term scheme run
by sane Christian people, which has been very helpful to him.

People like Dave cause an awful lot of trouble, you see.
There are people in the Church who've been getting away
with murder by making loud, confident statements about
what God will or won't do, without ever having to put their
money where their mouths are. Someone like Dave calls their

bluff. Terribly untidy, the Martins and Daves of this world.

I can't help thinking, Brad, that we're likely to be judged more on our compassion than our rightness. Would you rather arrive at the gates of heaven as a homosexual who had brought the love of God to people, or as a heterosexual with perfect theology who hadn't? I pray to God that I won't let him down in these matters, but I think they are far from clear.

Actually, your letter reached me at a time when my spiritual renaissance was dipping rather seriously. I had suddenly begun to feel very treacherous. Why wasn't I mourning for Gemma any more? How could I contemplate the idea of 'getting on with my life', as it's called, without her beside me? Hearing about poor Martin dragged me even further down, especially as things weren't going too well at church around then.

A little delegation of grim-faced gropers after grace (G-F-Gs after G) approached our vicar – a very good and long-suffering friend of mine, who is one of the most loving, godly characters you could imagine – to complain that our church was lagging behind one or two others in the town, where people were experiencing some new spiritual phenomenon that was 'sweeping the world'. Apparently it involves laughing and crying at the same time – we used to call it hysteria, but now, rather surprisingly, it's become a spiritual gift. Dear old Hector, the vicar, got quite upset about all this. Being the humble man he is, he troddled round to one of the local churches to check it out and, well, bring it back. The next Sunday in our church he prayed openly that if God wanted us to experience whatever this thing was, we might be ready to receive it. The G-F-Gs after G nearly bust a gut trying to receive it, but nothing really happened. Later, one of them suggested (in love, of course) that Hector was quenching the Spirit. What rubbish! That man couldn't quench a lighted match if he thought God was going to use it.

Things got pretty tense in the following week, with Hector

going through all sorts of self-doubt. By Friday evening, when we happened to have a visiting speaker booked to do his stuff in the church hall, he was quite low, and so was I. Everything seemed grey and useless and silly. I only went to support Hector because he'd arranged the evening, and I didn't want him to be upset by this little posse of disapprovers who were bound to be there, hoping to find further ammunition. Bradley, the speaker was a breath of fresh air from God. I've never seen Hector laugh as much or as loudly as he did that evening. In doing so, he burned his boats with the G-F-Gs after G, because one of the pieces that tickled him most was the following extract, transcribed faithfully from the tape of the evening:

'I'm so glad to be able to bring you wonderful news from my own parish of Punklethwaite! Few true believers can be unaware of the great waves of the Spirit that have passed through the worldwide Church in recent years, the famous "Tasmanian Tickle" to name but one. Now, it really does look as though my humble little fellowship has been divinely ordained to originate a new and powerful experience of the living presence of God. This thrilling phenomenon was originally manifested by Dora Cobbins (a lady whose antecedent proclivity towards manifestation has been well weighed), after a particularly piercing word from Sidney Barnside, who, as you may remember, was one of that little band known as the Punklethwaite Prophets. It was they who predicted revival throughout Punklethwaite within a month, and were proven to be absolutely right, provided crude criteria such as changed lives, commitment to Christ or attendance at a church were not used to define the term "revival".

This new, exciting phenomenon has been very aptly christened the "Punklethwaite Pant" by those of us who have been touched. My own experience – a typical one – was as follows.

After Sidney had shared from the front one Sunday, I became aware of a sensation which I can most easily describe as an alternate inflation and deflation of spongy tissue inside my chest, so that, as it were, air was passing in and out of my lungs, entering and escaping by way of the nose and mouth. I knew somehow in my spirit that this inner activity was centrally important to my well-being on the deepest level, and can you understand me when I say that I just didn't want it to stop – I wanted it to go on and on. After the service I told Sidney what had happened. He gently explained that I had received the gift of breathing, and suggested I go quietly home to seek guidance on the best way to use my gifting.

Since then the Punklethwaite Pant has spread like wildfire through Punklethwaite Minor, Punklethwaite Major, Upper Punklethwaite and Lower Punklethwaite. Every church seems to have a few who breathe, some, believe it or not, without even realizing that they have the gift.'

To say that the G-F-Gs after G were gobsmacked[1] is putting it mildly. They were furious! But everyone else loved it. Hector seemed to regain his sense of proportion that evening, and I thank God for that. I do believe, though, that a new denomination is about to be born in our town, and I'll bet you any money you like that they jolly soon acquire the gift of hysteria.

That evening meant a lot to me for another reason as well. Towards the end of his address, the speaker was talking about the Trinity and how difficult he's always found what all this three-in-one business means. Then he painted a little word picture for us. There was something about the sheer ordinariness and warmth of it that just melted me, and I've been more or less okay since then. This was what he said:

'It's late at night. Three figures are sitting around a campfire on the banks of the sea of Galilee, enjoying the way the sparks fly and the smell of freshly-caught fish sizzling over the flames. It's not a bottle party. Instead, the trio have contributed large measures of the grace, love and fellowship that are specialities of their particular house. The Father is an older man (well, be fair – he's got to be, hasn't he?), a bearded, deep-eyed, still personality, rich with potential for earth-shattering anger or extravagant, all-embracing love. He gazes into the flickering tongues of orange and red, his head filled with an eternity of thoughts.

Poking the embers with a long stick on the other side of the fire, in charge of the fish as usual because he has previous, hands-on experience, sits Jesus, the Son, the only one who has ever known or ever will know how it feels to be God with a real human skin. The marks of death are still on that skin, and will stay there until the victory that is already won has been claimed by the least, lost soul. He has a wonderful smile, laced with pain.

The third member of the party is more difficult to describe except that he is like one of the flames in the fire – vital and restless, beautiful, moving, constantly changing shape, alternately reflecting light and seeming to disappear into the shadows. The Holy Spirit is the one who is out and about and doing – but he does enjoy fish as well.

So, when the meal has been cooked and eaten, and the family gets down to business, what is the subject of their deep, intense, concerned conversation? The answer, believe it or not, dear friend, is that they are talking about – you.'

Really touched me . . .

Love, George

P.S. Hadn't you better call your father?

P.P.S. Great to hear about the response to the letters – is this a free magazine? Cherry needs shoes.

P.P.P.S. So did God really call you to be a minister or not?

Notes
[1]Gobsmacked, literally, means 'smacked in the mouth' = utterly surprised.

Dear George

It's late, but I'm wide awake and figured I'd use the time to write since I haven't heard from you in a couple of weeks.

First, business: You should've received a copy of February's *Today's Christian World* a few weeks ago and March's issue should arrive any day now (if it hasn't already). Andy assures me he sent them off. Finally, one of my letters made it in alongside yours after *two months* (not that I'm counting or anything). Andy has been editing them *very* carefully. He takes out the personal stuff and condenses the rest to whatever is funniest. Response from readers continues to be excellent. (Andy downplays it, of course. He's afraid it'll go to our heads.) If you haven't heard from Andy, let me know.

I'm up late because we had another Christians Anonymous meeting tonight. A couple of interesting things happened. Diane said she was confident 'in the Lord' that my mother would be completely healed. (Mom's health is getting worse now. She actually looks like she should have died weeks ago.) I thanked her and said I hoped she was right. Karen seemed preoccupied and didn't answer Dave's questions with her usual bumper-sticker insight. She asked us to pray for an 'unspoken request' (probably broke a nail).

Ruth asked us to pray for a friend at the office where she works. They had lunch together earlier in the week and Ruth believes she 'botched an opportunity to share her faith'. I don't know what that means. I find it hard to believe that Ruth could 'botch' anything. I told her so during our coffee break and her eyes welled up with tears. She said she 'just couldn't say the right things' to her friend and felt as uncomfortable as she ever felt in her life. I asked her what she expected would happen. She admitted to dreams of great eloquence – worthy of Peter at Pentecost or Paul at Mars' Hill – that would bring her friend to immediate salvation. Instead, she babbled and stammered and felt like a fool. Since that's my usual state, I wasn't sure why she was so upset.

Dave was surprisingly transparent that evening, too. Someone realized that he hadn't *really* told our group his answer to the question. 'Who are you as a Christian?' and we cornered him. He reluctantly admitted that, as leader of the group, he didn't think he should admit to the kinds of doubts he had. He knew it was one thing to talk about feelings and another to be honest about them. I had to think about the logic of his thinking for a few minutes.

Anyway, he said it all had to do with God's will. He wished he had some clear direction, but he didn't. In fact, his life, thus far, reflected that problem. He drifted from job to job after finishing college, never liking what he was doing, never really doing what he liked to do or what he felt called to do. Whatever his calling, he knew it certainly wasn't playing civil servant for a bunch of bureaucrats in the city.

'I'm a singer,' he said. 'The Lord gave me a song. But the Church wasn't ready for it.' Diane asked him how he knew that. 'Because none of them would book me,' he replied. 'My message was obviously too strong. A prophet is without honor in his own country. But I believe the Lord wants me to share my message with the world.'

I suggested that, maybe, he should start small – say, with our church – then build his ministry a little at a time. Dave was aghast, 'And restrict the talent God has given me? Limit his message? Think about Moses . . . Isaiah . . . Jeremiah . . .' I asked him what record company they recorded with. Dave didn't laugh. He takes few things more seriously than his calling. Or was it really his calling? That was the nagging question.

He went on to say that he's been singing the same song for five or six years now. He kept re-recording it to get the record companies interested. Country-western, pop, rock, rap – whatever was in, he adapted the song. He even won an award at the Sixteenth Annual Sonshine in the Mounties Christian Festival. Their brochures said it was his big chance to show what the Lord was doing in his life.

He sipped some coffee and continued. 'I was up against a woman who did a reggae gospel version of "Amazing Grace" and a Mick Jagger look-alike who did "How Majestic is your Name". She was pretty good.' We laughed, hoping it was a joke. 'I sang my heart out for the judges – vice presidents and executives of various Christian record companies and music publishers. It was my big moment. They looked bored, but I won. I even got to sing again for everyone at the festival on the last night. They put me on last. It was midnight and nearly everyone had gone home. But I sang my song. Then I went home and waited for the calls.' They didn't come. Dave went back to work like always. 'I just wish I could figure out why God called me to a full-time career as a Christian singing star and won't get me an audience,' he said. 'Don't get me wrong, I'll do what he wants me to do. But . . . I wonder about it sometimes.'

That's all from me. I hope you're doing okay – and that your silence isn't indicative of something . . . (I can never be sure with you.)

Tag. You're it.

Brad

February 6th

Dear George

Our letters crossed in the mail. Sorry about that. I should've waited. Funny – and sad – that we could write on the same day about two different Daves and their struggles. Now I've lost track of where we are. It's been a very strange week.

First, business again: I think you better deal with Andy directly about the letters he's published and the money he owes you. I hate to say so, but I think it's time you invested in a fax machine. I assume such technology exists in England – even if Sears doesn't. Also, it looks like I'll be flying back over for this year's ICE (23–26 March), depending on how things are with Mom. Are you going? You better! Is it crassly American to say that I'm looking forward to seeing you?

I love the term 'gobsmacked'. I want to use it in conversation more often.

Mom is on her last legs. The hospice people are preparing to come in for twelve-hour shifts, more if necessary.

Which brings me to the next twist in the story . . . I was just getting ready to go visit Mom when Karen (from Christians Anonymous) surprised me with a visit. She was more nervous and high-strung than I'd seen her before. She said, in a very long sentence, that she wanted to talk to me because I was the only one who might understand because my mother was seriously ill and she didn't know where else to go and . . . then she started to cry. I invited her in, sat her down and uncomfortably asked her what was wrong.

Her husband left her. In broken sobs, she gave me as many details as she could. She had gone home after last week's meeting to find him at the front door with his suitcases. He was upset because she had come home early. He didn't want to face her. He had said his goodbyes in a note left on her pillow. Karen couldn't mask her shock. Admittedly, things hadn't been good between them for a while (thus the guarded prayer requests in our group), but they had agreed to start marriage counseling together. Her husband said it was too late for counseling. He simply didn't love her anymore. Karen pleaded with him to stay, to work things out. God could help them if they would only put their trust in him. Her husband said he knew all the clichés and would let his lawyer work out the details. Then he left.

I can't begin to tell you how I felt, George. All this time I've been judging her, criticizing her, making fun of her 'simplistic' Christianity, while she was at home trying to deal with the breakdown of the most important thing in her life. She cried again and I held her like a little baby. I very nearly spouted off all the mindless clichés I so callously accused her of using, but I bit my tongue. All I could think to do was keep my mouth shut and pray. That was a tough thing to do since I first had to repent for being so hard-hearted about her. I was an idiot for believing the appearances she gave of living in a perfect world.

You once made a sharp remark (one among many) in one of your letters about how people in America look down on divorced people. In an instant, my mind raced to the battle Karen has ahead of her – not only dealing with the loss of her husband, but the stigma that'll come from her loss. Even if she does everything she can to save her marriage, even if it wasn't her fault, even if she remains a 'divorced widow' for the rest of her life – she'll always be the 'Oh, she's divorced' woman in our church, and many churches like it. I know firsthand. People said it enough about my mother after my father ran off.

But like our letters about homosexuality, I don't know how to respond. In this country we've had a number of very prominent Christian leaders and celebrities who were brought down either by a temptation they used to preach against or because their marriages ended. What are we supposed to do with them? On one side of the debate, I can understand those who maintain that the fallen leaders should resign their positions, publicly repent and disappear from the public eye for a time of restoration. On the other side of the debate, I understand those who say it isn't our place to judge them, but that we should merely pray for them. One side wants to follow Church discipline as prescribed in the New Testament. The other side calls that being heartless and without compassion.

And there's a third party that says, 'See? Even your big-name Christian celebrities don't believe in your Christianity enough to live it out.' That's the real problem, isn't it? None of us really believes in our Christianity enough to live it out.

I'm not sure how we'll be judged by God in the end – for having too much compassion or not enough backbone to stand for what we believe. Jesus did both: stood his ground with great compassion. I don't know how to do that, George. All I know is that I held Karen like a little baby, kept my mouth shut and felt like a fool for having ever judged her about anything. What would you have done?

Tag. You're it.

Brad

11 *February*

Dear Brad

My silence is not 'indicative of something' as you so ponderously put it. The fact is, we sat down on exactly the same day to write to each other. So this letter is not a reply to the letter that you'll write in reply to the letter that I wrote at the same time as you, but a reply to the letter that you wrote to me at the same time as I was writing a letter to you in reply to the letter before that. I guess we just have to live in the mystery, don't we?

I am much amused to hear that Andy is taking out the personal stuff and condensing the rest to whatever is funniest. That'll mean that your letters stay exactly the same and mine hardly appear at all. Only joking, Bradley. I'm glad we've become co-writers now. I got the February magazine with the letter about Anglicanism. What a load of rubbish – my bit, I mean. I felt quite ashamed. If I were Andy, I'd make this a very short series indeed.

Your Bible study group sounds like most Bible study groups I've ever been involved with – a bunch of wistful children playing at a sort of Lego-style Christianity, using brightly coloured easy-to-fix bricks and hoping everything will be all right when something serious and grown-up has to be built. I don't mean that to sound sarcastic or critical. I feel sorry for them all, I really do: Karen's tentative 'unspoken request' (I'd be surprised if it *was* something trivial), poor little Ruth's 'botched opportunity' and Dave's disappointment over the progress of his international singing career. Oh, Brad, don't you wish sometimes that

Jesus would pop down in the flesh for five minutes to sort a few things out?

'Ah, but he is here,' whispers the parsonical voice of my evangelical upbringing. 'Don't you think it's just a little ungrateful and unfaithful to express that sort of wish?' One of my ambitions is to stick a nail into the end of a very heavy wooden club and hit the parsonical voice of my evangelical upbringing with it. Unfortunately, the parsonical voice of my evangelical upbringing wouldn't allow me to do a thing like that. I really want my relationship with God to be honest and open this time round, but a lot of the time I feel as if one of Spiderman's nets is holding my brain down. I'm excited as well, though, because

You'll never know what I'm excited about, Bradley, because just as I'd finished typing the word 'because', I heard the second post arrive. Now, on the table before me, I have your reply to the letter that I sent on the same day as the letter that you sent, to which this letter was a reply, but is now also a letter replying to your reply to my letter. The mystery deepens.

Thanks for the stuff about Andy. Thanks particularly for your magnificent offer to buy me a fax machine. There's a rather smart, third-hand, steam-operated model in the old thatched computer cottage in the High Street. A bit smelly and noisy, but perfectly usable. I think they want £5 13s 6½d' for it. I'm sure they'll take a Sears token.

Of course I'm going to the ICE this year, and it's not crass for an American to say he's looking forward to seeing someone – just unusual. Seriously, I hope you'll come and stay with Cherry and I for at least one night while you're over here. I guess, though, that with your mother as ill as she is, there's a fair chance you won't come at all. Let's just wait and see how things work out. We still pray for Mary every evening. So sorry you and she have to live through this time.

What would I have done with Karen? The same. Same

confusion, same guilt. Is it really true that we don't believe in our Christianity enough to live it out? It probably is true, but saying that seems to me to avoid some of the really tough questions that I'm determined to tackle over the next few months. Does our experience of God match up with what we've been taught our experience of God should be? Does anyone's? If not, why not? Have we misunderstood what being a Christian means?

Should we make a poem out of the thin gruel of what's happened to us (it's quite fashionable to do that nowadays, isn't it?), when there may be a good meal to be had if we knew where to look?

We'll sort the world out if you come over in March – no problem!

Love, George

P.S. Hadn't you better call your father?

Notes:
¹£5 13s 6½d = five pounds, thirteen shillings and six and a half pence. British currency was modernized in the early seventies and no longer includes shillings.

February 21st

Dear George

I wish you were here. My mother died last night. In the last week her health worsened and – oh, never mind. I can't write. I'll call you.

[Editor's Note: Brad phoned George (forgetting the seven-hour difference in time and awakening George at two o'clock in the morning). We don't have a transcript of the conversation and Brad can only remember summarizing for George the circumstances leading up to his mother's death. Her health had suddenly deteriorated significantly and hospice nurses specializing in cancer victims began round-the-clock care at her home. Brad moved in. When the nurses realized that she might not survive beyond the next couple of days, Brad then called his half-brother and half-sisters. The family rallied around Mary's bedside and prayed for her. She slipped into a coma and died the next evening. Brad obviously started and stopped this letter repeatedly over the days that followed.]

February 25th

I just found this letter and figured I should finish it now that I think I can. Thanks for talking to me on the phone (even though I woke you up). Everything's a haze now, like somebody pulled a thick wool sock over my brain, which is why I want to write now before everything slips into dull memory.

I told you the facts behind Mom's death, but I thought

you'd like to know some of the details. After Tom, Cindy and Melanie (my half-siblings) arrived on their various flights from around the country, we held a vigil around Mom's bed. At a time like that, I was so thankful I'm part of a Christian family. I've been bothered in the past by what I thought was their evasion of dealing with Mom's cancer. I see now that it was just hard for them to connect to what was happening to Mom while living out their own lives so far away.

We read scripture to her and prayed and reminisced. Tom, Cindy and Melanie encouraged Mom that their dad was waiting for her on the other side and what a sweet reunion that would be. I confess that I felt a little resentful and jealous because I didn't know their father at all. He seemed to be such a wonderful, godly man – in contrast to *my* father, who turned out to be such a first-class jerk. (Yes, I actually called to let him know about Mom. I got his answering machine, as expected, and left a quick message. I haven't heard back. I'm sure he'll miss the funeral.) Mom wasn't responsive. She simply smiled and nodded a couple of times. She chose not to talk, or maybe couldn't talk by that time.

On the second day, the hospice people couldn't figure out how she was lasting so long. We (the children) talked about it and decided she was hanging on for some reason. So we prayed that she would let go – let God take her home. There was nothing left to hang on to.

On the morning of the third day, I was reading Psalm 23 to her – it was always one of her favorites – and she gently squeezed my hand without opening her eyes. It suddenly dawned on me why she might be hanging on, so I leaned over and whispered in her ear to let go. She didn't have to worry about me (her baby), I would be all right. It was all right for her to let go.

She slipped into a coma that afternoon.

Still, we kept up our vigil of praying and reading scripture and singing her favorite hymns. Later the next evening she surprised us by opening her eyes. 'Oh my!' she exclaimed, then closed her eyes and . . . died.

I was so relieved that it took another day for the reality to hit me – she's gone. She's with Jesus, I know, but there's now a very large emptiness where she used to be. I'm not sure how I'll cope with that.

The morning of the funeral I couldn't work out little details. I shaved twice without meaning to. I sat on the edge of my bed and stared at my socks for fifteen minutes. I turned on the stereo and punched the button to play a cassette, forgetting what I had left in the machine. It was a tape Diane had given to me several weeks before to encourage me about Mom. An Evangelist Diane loved was shouting something about Christians today not knowing what they want from God. Christians today are lacking in faith, he said, they don't believe that Jesus'll give us whatever we ask for. 'Ask! What do you want from God? What do you want? Answer that question then ask God for it. Whatever it is, he'll give it to you. This is what Satan wants to keep from you. This is the power he wants to yank out of your hands,' he said.

Outside, it started to snow. I sat down and stared at my socks some more while the tape spun on. 'Ask and you'll receive,' he said. 'You want healing? Ask for it! Someone you love sick and dying? Ask for their healing! God'll give it to you! I've spoken with him . . . I know it from his word! Ask – and you'll receive. Anything –' All I wanted to ask then was whether to wear blue socks or black. Mom was dead and I was going to say goodbye to that fragile shell before the lid closed and the ground covered it up. Blue socks or black? I checked myself in the mirror and didn't like what I was wearing. I would've changed for the third time that morning if Tom hadn't come to pick me up.

I complained to him that I didn't have anything to wear for a funeral. 'You can wear whatever you want,' he said.

'You don't think this suit is too . . . too flashy?' I remember saying, 'They dressed Mom in her best dress. She'll look good. Like she did for church.'

'Don't worry about it. You look fine.' He took me by the shoulders and looked me square in the eyes, 'We're burying our mother today. Nobody cares how we look.' I nodded and lost it for a minute – crying stupidly. Tom hugged me with those big arms of his and it struck me that it was the first time we had ever hugged, or that he had ever referred to Mom as *our* mom, which moved me to cry longer and even more stupidly.

Before we left, I turned off the tape. Tom asked what kind of garbage I was listening to. I told him it was a tape from a friend of mine who was convinced Mom would be healed. 'She *is* healed.' Tom said. 'Just not the way we expected.'

Diane was at the funeral. She was there with the rest of the Christians Anonymous gang. She had called the church and said she was a friend of mine and volunteered to sing if they needed someone. She had a wonderful voice. She sang 'A Mighty Fortress is our God'.

There's a lot of work to be done in the days ahead – selling Mom's house, sorting through her belongings, etc. I'm not looking forward to it.

I was right about my dad. He didn't call, he didn't show up for the funeral.

134

3 March

Dear Brad

Last night Cherry and I decided it was time your mum came visiting. You're going to think we're a real pair of idiots, but I'll tell you what we did, anyway.

It was one of those drizzly, grey days – very cold and bleak, real end of the winter sort of stuff. We had hot tomato soup and bacon sandwiches for tea. Then we dressed up warm in jumpers and coats and scarves and pulled my cranky old handcart down to the woods behind Cherry's school. There is lots of dead wood lying around down there, and we soon had a whole cart-load to take back home. It was a sort of sacrament for little Cherry, Brad. Every single piece of wood that she collected was special – chosen to be part of remembering your mum. She wanted to be sure about every twig and log. 'Is this all right, Daddy? Do you think this'll burn nicely? Is it too big? Have we got enough small bits now?' You never saw anyone take anything as seriously as Cherry took that gathering of fuel for the lighting of a flame to celebrate the life and death of someone she'd never met.

We dragged the cart back home and carried the wood, armful by armful, into the study. Then we sat together on the carpet making paper-rolls our of sheets from old *Independent* newspapers to get the fire going with.

Cherry and I really know about making paper-rolls, Brad.

Next, we piled wood on top of the rolls and Cherry lit the paper with some specially long, extra-safe matches. Do you know about log fires? They work magic. When they flare up, a dark, dank room suddenly turns into the cosiest place in the world. I turned off the central light and put one of the side lamps on while Cherry used another of those long matches to light our two big, fat white candles that have *never* been lit before.

I smoothed the seat of the beaten-up armchair with the rust-coloured covers then sat on my swivel chair to wait for Cherry, who'd gone off to the kitchen to make three drinks. She insisted there had to be three. She came back with a coffee for me, a glass of Ribena¹ for her and a cup of hot chocolate for Mary, your mum. She put it on a little table by the armchair and finally sat on the floor by my feet, sipping her drink and gazing into the fire.

Bradley, your mum was here last night, just as we hoped she would be. I don't mean that we saw her or that she spoke to us, or anything like that. I just mean that she came visiting and was with us, was grateful for the fire and the candles and the gentle affection of a little girl who had never seen her, and even for the hot chocolate – even if she couldn't actually drink it.

Later, as I blew the candles out and turned off the lamp, I said a proper goodbye to Gemma for the first time. She was so relieved, Brad, so very relieved.

When I was tucking Cherry up later, she said, just before turning over to go to sleep, 'Daddy, Bradley and I are the same, aren't we?'

'How so, darling?' I asked.

'We've both lost our mummies, haven't we?'

'Yes, darling,' I said, 'both of you, yes.'

'But they know each other now, don't they, Daddy? Do you think they talk about us a lot?'

'A lot, sweetheart,' I whispered, 'always talking about us – always.'

'I don't remember Mummy, Daddy. She loved me, didn't she?'

'Yes.'

'Like Bradley's mummy loved him.'

'Yes.'
'Goodnight, Daddy.'
'Goodnight, Cherry.'
Goodnight, Gemma. Goodnight, Mary.
God bless you, Brad.

Love, George and Cherry

Notes:
¹ In Britain, 'Ribena' is a blackcurrant drink.

Dear George

It seems like such a short time ago that I was standing next to Mom's bedside, praying for her to let go so she could be with Jesus. And it seems like forever since she left. Now I want her back, wishing I'd never encouraged her to leave me and that I had had the ability to touch her thin and shriveled body and heal her fully so we could spend Sunday afternoons together like we did before. I could get annoyed like I did so many times before, and we could argue knowing that our arguing was a disguise for our inadequacy at expressing love.

Then I remember that Lazarus was raised but had to die again. I don't think I would want to put her through that. It's better that I'm patient and wait to see her on the other side.

Do I sound like I have it in perspective? Hm . . . It's a lie. I'll celebrate her homecoming but I'll be damned if I'll celebrate my loss. It's been awful and I miss her. More than I ever would have imagined.

There have been glimmers, though . . . of hope. Your letter was one. And some sweet treasures emerged from sorting through Mom's things. One surprise was her prayer journal. She'd been keeping it for years and none of us knew. It was fascinating to go back through periods of our lives and read what she thought about them in the context of her praying.

Most interesting were those times when her prayers didn't line up with our memories. For example, Tom remembered going through a very rebellious time as a teenager, causing no end of problems for Mom and his dad. He was convinced, like most teens, that his parents were out of touch with reality, completely oblivious to how he felt. One night he came home extremely late and Mom went ballistic on him. He went to his room and thought about running away from home. But while he waited to make sure that Mom and his dad were asleep, he fell asleep, too. Morning came and all his feelings about running away had gone. Nothing was said about the incident from the night before.

But Mom's prayer journal entry that night went on for page after page as she literally cried before God to help Tom get through this period. She knew how Tom felt, she wrote, and prayed that God wouldn't let him make any long-term decisions on short-term adolescent urges. The entry continued in that vein until it became clear to all of us that she had written it while sitting next to the front door the entire night – certain as she was that Tom might run away.

Tom was gobsmacked (as you would say) that Mom knew him so well at a time he was convinced she didn't know him at all.

Each of us encountered similar experiences while reading through her journals. She had far more insight than any of us would've given her credit for. She prayed earnestly about things we never *dreamed* she knew about, like Cindy's brief relationship with an older married man or Melanie's struggle with the boss who wanted her to do some questionably ethical things in their business. How did she know? We couldn't begin to guess. Eyes in the back of her spiritual head.

There was also the entry chronicling her first husband's death – and the flower-shaped tear-stain in the ink.

As for me, I was most touched by her prayers for my *ministry*. You know, I've spent my whole life convinced that I failed her because I became a writer instead of a pastor. But her prayers were that God would use me in *whatever* way he wanted. It didn't matter whether I was a pastor or not. She later wrote to thank God for my writing – and said how proud of me she was. I was bothered at first because I wished she had simply come out and told me. But then I realized that she *had* told me – in a number of different ways and in numerous conversations – but I was convinced she was just saying it without meaning it. Her journal proved me wrong.

Her latest entries included prayers for you and Cherry, George. Her entry from February 4th said that she was sorry she wouldn't get to meet you before she died. But she knew she'd see you later – and Gemma sooner. Based on your 'sacrament', I'm sure she will.

Thank you. Thank Cherry.

Love, Brad

P.S. The plans are all made for coming back to the ICE. I arrive the morning of the 23rd.

P.P.S. George, I've been thinking about it. When we meet at that pub in Haywards Heath, you *have to* explain to me what the expression 'tally-ho, pip, pip' means. You never did. And if you don't know, then ask Cherry. I'm sure she'll make up a wonderful answer.

16 *March*

Dear Brad

We've come a long way, haven't we, Bradawl? I had a look at
my early letters to you the other day. What a caustic, bitter
little person I was. We've both come a long way in a year, but
don't get too relaxed – you're still an American, when all's
said and done, so there's a long way to go yet. When we meet
I shall be interested to find out if you're still consuming
alcohol in the same quantities as before. Also, one or two of
your theological creases definitely need ironing out. I'll see
to it – don't worry. Your mum's a hard act to follow, judging
by your last letter (isn't the prayer diary wonderful?) but
you'll get there in the end. We'll both get there in the end –
thanks to Jesus. I may not be speaking in tongues again yet,
but at least I'm speaking to Him.

My favourite part of the Church calendar is coming up
soon: Easter. Crucifixion, resurrection and Easter eggs. I'm
so glad we don't have to earn our way into heaven, Bradley.
You and I would be out for a start. I wrote something for this
Easter. It's a reminder that none of us can judge anyone else
– one of your besetting sins, I believe . . .

> Within my sacred heart
> I headed up the holocaust
> Perpetrated endless petty meannesses
> On Sunday afternoons in Peckham Rye
> Murdered frightened children on the moors
> Didn't give the mower back
> Calmly supervised the killing fields

Cheated British Rail
I watched the blank-eyed starving babies die
And sulked because there was no ginger ale
Do not think such perfect circles end
Do not think they start
Think only that I hold you all
Within my sacred heart.

You haven't forgotten where the Red Lion is, have you? See you Friday . . .

George

THE SACRED DIARY OF ADRIAN PLASS
AGED 37¾

Illustrated by Dan Donovan
Adrian Plass

A full-length, slide-splitting paperback based on the hilarious diary entries in Christian Family magazine of Adrian Plass, 'an amiable but somewhat inept Christian'. By his own confession, Adrian 'makes many mistakes and is easily confused', but a reassuring sense of belonging to the family of God is the solid, underlying theme.

THE GROWING UP PAINS OF ADRIAN PLASS

Adrian Plass

When TV viewers in the south tuned into 'Company', they could eavesdrop on a few friends enjoying some late night conversation around a kitchen table. For Adrian Plass, the programme is a landmark in his Christian life. With disarming frankness and irresistible humour, he unfolds his own story and that of some of the programme's memorable guests, such as David Watson, cleaning lady Jo Williams and Auschwitz survivor, Rabbi Hugo Grynn.

THE HORIZONTAL EPISTLES OF ANDROMEDA VEAL

Illustrated by Dan Donovan
Adrian Plass

Adrian Plass, diary-writer *sans pareil* returns! This time he finds much to amuse him in the letters of Andromeda Veal, precocious eleven year old daughter of a Greenham woman, and shrewd commentator on her local church and the wider world.

Andromeda is in hospital with an undisclosed complaint. She seizes her chance to write all those letters that had to wait before – to, 'Gorgeous Chops', 'Ray Gun', 'Rabbit' Runcie, the Pope, and even Cliff Richard.

At the same time her friends of Sacred Diary fame write to her: Gerald with his mysterious 'persunnal problem', Mrs. Flushpool, Leonard Thin, and also the local MP who vows that she 'can be sick in our hands'! She is also the lucky recipient of letters from conscientious Bible student Charles Cooke who finds 15 texts for every word of 'I hope you get better soon', and a large Christian organization whose aims appear to change from letter to letter. Of course Andromeda's illness gives her a chance to think more seriously about God too, even to the extent of writing him a letter.

All of this is interspersed with new diary entries from Adrian Plass's inimitable diary writer and Dan Donovan's hilarious illustrations.